REPORT FROM
IRON MOUNTAIN

REPORT FROM
IRON MOUNTAIN
ON THE
POSSIBILITY
AND
DESIRABILITY
OF
PEACE

WITH INTRODUCTORY MATERIAL BY
LEONARD C. LEWIN

THE DIAL PRESS, INC. 1967 NEW YORK

CONTENTS

FOREWORD

"John Doe," as I will call him in this book for reasons that will be made clear, is a professor at a large university in the Middle West. His field is one of the social sciences, but I will not identify him beyond this. He telephoned me one evening last winter, quite unexpectedly; we had not been in touch for several years. He was in New York for a few days, he said, and there was something important he wanted to discuss with me. He wouldn't say what it was. We met for lunch the next day at a midtown restaurant.

He was obviously disturbed. He made small talk for half an hour, which was quite out of character, and I didn't press him. Then, apropos of nothing, he mentioned a dispute between a writer and a prominent political family that had been in the headlines. What, he wanted to know, were my views on "freedom of information"? How would I qualify them? And so on. My answers were not memorable, but they seemed to satisfy him. Then, quite abruptly, he began to tell me the following story:

Early in August of 1963, he said, he found a message on his desk that a "Mrs. Potts" had called him from Washington. When he returned the call, a *man* answered immediately, and told Doe, among other things, that he had been selected to serve on a commission "of the highest importance." Its objective was *to determine, accurately and realistically, the nature of the problems that would confront the United States if and when a condition of "permanent peace" should arrive, and to draft a program for dealing with this contingency.* The man described the unique procedures that were to govern the commission's work and that were expected to extend its scope far beyond that of any previous examination of these problems.

Considering that the caller did not precisely identify either himself or his agency, his persuasiveness must have been of a truly remarkable order. Doe entertained no serious doubts of the *bona fides* of the project, however, chiefly because of his previous experience with the excessive secrecy that often surrounds quasi-governmental activities. In addition, the man at the other end of the line demonstrated an impressively complete and surprisingly detailed knowledge of Doe's work and personal life. He also mentioned the names of others who were to serve with the group; most of them were known to Doe by reputation. Doe agreed to take the assignment —he felt he had no real choice in the matter—and to appear the second Saturday following at Iron Mountain, New York. An airline ticket arrived in his mail the next morning.

The cloak-and-dagger tone of this convocation was further enhanced by the meeting place itself. Iron Mountain, located near the town of Hudson, is like something out of Ian Fleming or E. Phillips Oppenheim. It is an underground nuclear hideout for hundreds of large American corporations. Most of them use it as an emergency storage vault for important documents. But a number of them maintain substitute corporate headquarters as well, where essential personnel could presumably survive and continue to work after an attack. This latter group includes such firms as Standard Oil of New Jersey, Manufacturers Hanover Trust, and Shell.

I will leave most of the story of the operations of the Special Study Group, as the commission was formally called, for Doe to tell in his own words ("Background Information"). At this point it is necessary to say only that it met and worked regularly for over two and a half years, after which it produced a Report. It was this document, and what to do about it, that Doe wanted to talk to me about.

The Report, he said, had been suppressed—both by the Special Study Group itself and by the government interagency committee to which it had been submitted. After months of agonizing, Doe had decided that he would no longer be party to keeping it secret. What he wanted from me was advice and assistance in having it published. He gave me his copy to read, with the express understanding that if for any reason I were unwilling to become involved, I would say nothing about it to anyone else.

I read the Report that same night. I will pass over my own reactions to it, except to say that the unwillingness of Doe's associates to publicize their findings became readily understandable. What had happened was that they had been so tenacious in their determination to deal *comprehensively* with the many problems of transition to peace that the original questions asked of them were never quite answered. Instead, this is what they concluded:

Lasting peace, while not theoretically impossible, is probably unattainable; even if it could be achieved it would almost certainly not be in the best interests of a stable society to achieve it.

That is the gist of what they say. Behind their qualified academic language runs this general argument: War fills certain functions essential to the stability of our society; until other ways of filling them are developed, the war system must be maintained—and improved in effectiveness.

It is not surprising that the Group, in its Letter of Transmittal, did not choose to justify its work to "the lay reader, unexposed to the exigencies of higher political or military responsibility." Its Report was addressed, deliberately, to unnamed government administrators of high rank; it assumed considerable political sophistication from this select audience. To the general reader, therefore, the substance of the document may be even more unsettling than its conclusions. He may not be prepared for some of its assumptions—for instance, that most medical advances are viewed more as problems than as progress; or that poverty is necessary and desirable, public postures by politicians to the contrary notwithstanding; or that standing armies are, among other things, social-welfare institutions in exactly the same sense as are old-people's homes and mental hospitals. It may strike him as odd to find the probable explanation of "flying saucer" incidents disposed of *en passant* in less than a sentence. He may be less surprised to find that the space program and the "controversial" antimissile missile and fallout shelter programs are understood to have the spending of vast sums of money, not the advancement of science or national defense, as their principal goals, and to learn that "military" draft policies are only remotely concerned with defense.

He may be offended to find the organized repression of minority groups, and even the reestablishment of slavery, seriously (and on the whole favorably) discussed as possible aspects of a world at peace. He is not likely to take kindly to the notion of the *deliberate* intensification of air and water pollution (as part of a program leading to peace), even when the reason for considering it is made clear. That a world without war will have to turn sooner rather than later to universal test-tube procreation will be less disturbing, if no more appealing.

But few readers will not be taken aback, at least, by a few
lines in the Report's conclusions, repeated in its formal
recommendations, that suggest that the long-range planning—and "budgeting"—of the "optimum" number of
lives to be destroyed annually in overt warfare is high
on the Group's list of priorities for government action.

I cite these few examples primarily to warn the general reader what he can expect. The statesmen and strategists for whose eyes the Report was intended obviously
need no such protective admonition.

This book, of course, is evidence of my response to
Doe's request. After carefully considering the problems
that might confront the publisher of the Report, we took
it to The Dial Press. There, its significance was immediately recognized, and, more important, we were given
firm assurances that no outside pressures of any sort
would be permitted to interfere with its publication.

It should be made clear that Doe does not disagree
with the substance of the Report, which represents a
genuine consensus in all important respects. He constituted a minority of one—but only on the issue of dis-
closing it to the general public. A look at how the Group
dealt with *this* question will be illuminating.

The debate took place at the Group's last full meeting before the Report was written, late in March, 1966,
and again at Iron Mountain. Two facts must be kept in
mind, by way of background. The first is that the Special
Study Group had never been explicitly charged with or
sworn to secrecy, either when it was convened or at any

time thereafter. The second is that the Group had nevertheless operated *as if* it had been. This was assumed from the circumstances of its inception and from the tone of its instructions. (The Group's acknowledgment of help from "the many persons . . . who contributed so greatly to our work" is somewhat equivocal; these persons were not told the nature of the project for which their special resources of information were solicited.)

Those who argued the case for keeping the Report secret were admittedly motivated by fear of the explosive political effects that could be expected from publicity. For evidence, they pointed to the suppression of the far less controversial report of then-Senator Hubert Humphrey's subcommittee on disarmament in 1962. (Subcommittee members had reportedly feared that it might be used by Communist propagandists, as Senator Stuart Symington put it, to "back up the Marxian theory that war production was the reason for the success of capitalism.") Similar political precautions had been taken with the better-known Gaither Report in 1957, and even with the so-called Moynihan Report in 1965.

Furthermore, they insisted, a distinction must be made between serious studies, which are normally classified unless and until policy makers decide to release them, and conventional "showcase" projects, organized to demonstrate a political leadership's concern about an issue and to deflect the energy of those pressing for action on it. (The example used, because some of the Group had participated in it, was a "White House Conference" on international cooperation, disarmament, etc., which had been staged late in 1965 to offset complaints about escalation of the Vietnam war.)

Doe acknowledges this distinction, as well as the strong possibility of public misunderstanding. But he feels that if the sponsoring agency had wanted to *mandate* secrecy it could have done so at the outset. It could also have assigned the project to one of the government's established "think tanks," which normally work on a classified basis. He scoffed at fear of public reaction, which could have no lasting effect on long-range measures that might be taken to implement the Group's proposals, and derided the Group's abdication of responsibility for its opinions and conclusions. So far as he was concerned, there was such a thing as a public *right* to know what was being done on its behalf; the burden of proof was on those who would abridge it.

If my account seems to give Doe the better of the argument, despite his failure to convince his colleagues, so be it. My participation in this book testifies that I am not neutral. In my opinion, the decision of the Special Study Group to censor its own findings was not merely timid but presumptuous. But the refusal, as of this writing, of the agencies for which the Report was prepared to release it themselves raises broader questions of public policy. Such questions center on the continuing use of self-serving definitions of "security" to avoid possible political embarrassment. It is ironic how often this practice backfires.

I should state, for the record, that I do not share the

attitudes toward war and peace, life and death, and survival of the species manifested in the Report. Few readers will. In human terms, it is an outrageous document. But it does represent a serious and challenging effort to define an enormous problem. And it explains, or certainly appears to explain, aspects of American policy otherwise incomprehensible by the ordinary standards of common sense. What we may think of these explanations is something else, but it seems to me that we are entitled to know not only what they are but whose they are.

By "whose" I don't mean merely the names of the authors of the Report. Much more important, we have a right to know to what extent their assumptions of social necessity are shared by the decision-makers in our government. Which do they accept and which do they reject? However disturbing the answers, only full and frank discussion offers any conceivable hope of solving the problems raised by the Special Study Group in their Report from Iron Mountain.

L.C.L.

New York, June 1967

BACKGROUND INFORMATION

[*The following account of the workings of the Special Study Group is taken verbatim from a series of tape-recorded interviews I had with "John Doe." The transcript has been edited to minimize the intrusion of my questions and comments, as well as for length, and the sequence has been revised in the interest of continuity.* L.C.L.]

How was the Group formed?

. . . The general idea for it, for this *kind* of study, dates back at least to 1961. It started with some of the new people who came in with the Kennedy administration, mostly, I think, with McNamara, Bundy, and Rusk. They were impatient about many things. . . . One of them was that no really serious work had been done about planning for peace—a long-range peace, that is, with long-range planning.

Everything that had been written on the subject [before 1961] was superficial. There was insufficient appreciation of the scope of the problem. The main reason for this, of course, was that the idea of a *real* peace in the world, general disarmament and so on, was looked on as utopian. Or even crackpot. This is still true, and it's easy enough to understand when you look at what's going on in the world today. . . . It was reflected in the studies that had been made up to that time. They were not realistic. . . .

The idea of the Special Study, the exact form it would take, was worked out early in '63. . . . The settlement of the Cuban missile affair had something to do with it, but what helped most to get it moving were the big changes in military spending that were being planned. . . . Plants being closed, relocations, and so forth. Most of it wasn't made public until much later. . . .

[I understand] it took a long time to select the people for the Group. The calls didn't go out until the summer. . . .

Who made the selection?

That's something I can't tell you. I wasn't involved with the preliminary planning. The first I knew of it was when I was called myself. But three of the people had been in on it, and what the rest of us know we learned from them, about what went on earlier. I do know that it started very informally. I don't know what particular government agency approved the project.

Would you care to make a guess?

All right—I think it was an *ad hoc* committee, at the cabinet level, or near it. It had to be. I suppose they gave the organizational job—making arrangements, paying the bills, and so on—to somebody from State or Defense or the National Security Council. Only one of us was in touch with Washington, and I wasn't the one. But I can tell you that very, very few people knew about us. . . . For instance, there was the Ackley Committee.[1] It was set up *after* we were. If you read their report— the same old tune—economic reconversion, turning sword plants into plowshare factories—I think you'll wonder if even the President knew about our Group. The Ackley Committee certainly didn't.

Is that possible, really? I mean that not even the President knew of your commission?

Well, I don't think there's anything odd about the government attacking a problem at two different levels. Or even about two or three [government] agencies working at cross-purposes. It happens all the time. Perhaps the President did know. And I don't mean to denigrate the Ackley Committee, but it was exactly that *narrowness*

---

[1] This was a "Committee on the Economic Impact of Defense and Disarmament," headed by Gardner Ackley, of the Council of Economic Advisers. It was established by Presidential order in December, 1963, and issued a report in July, 1965.

of approach that we were supposed to get away from. . . .

You have to remember—you've read the Report—that what they wanted from us was a different kind of *thinking*. It was a matter of approach. Herman Kahn calls it "Byzantine"—no agonizing over cultural and religious values. No moral posturing. It's the kind of thinking that Rand and the Hudson Institute and I.D.A.[2] brought into *war* planning. . . . What they asked us to do, and I think we did it, was to give the same kind of treatment to the hypothetical problems of peace as they give to a hypothetical nuclear war. . . . We may have gone further than they expected, but once you establish your premises and your logic you can't turn back. . . .

Kahn's books,[3] for example, are misunderstood, at least by laymen. They shock people. But you see, what's important about them is not his conclusions, or his opinions. It's the *method*. He has done more than anyone else I can think of to get the general public accustomed to the *style* of modern military thinking. . . . Today it's possible for a columnist to write about "counterforce strategy" and "minimum deterrence" and "credible first-strike capability" without having to explain every other word. He can write about war and strategy without getting bogged down in questions of morality. . . .

The other big difference about our work is breadth. The Report speaks for itself. I can't say that we took

[2] The Institute for Defense Analysis.
[3] *On Thermonuclear War, Thinking About the Unthinkable, On Escalation.*

every relevant aspect of life and society into account, but I don't think we missed anything essential. . . .

Why was the project given to an outside commission? Why couldn't it have been handled directly by an appropriate government agency?

I think that's obvious, or should be. The kind of thinking wanted from our Group just isn't to be had in a formal government operation. Too many constraints. Too many inhibitions. This isn't a new problem. Why else would outfits like Rand and Hudson stay in business? Any assignment that's at all sophisticated is almost always given to an outside group. This is true even in the State Department, in the "gray" operations, those that are supposed to be unofficial, but are really as official as can be. Also with the C.I.A. . . .

For our study, even the private research centers were too institutional. . . . A lot of thought went into making sure that *our* thinking would be unrestricted. All kinds of little things. The way we were called into the Group, the places we met, all kinds of subtle devices to remind us. For instance, even our name, the Special Study Group. You know government names. Wouldn't you think we'd have been called "Operation Olive Branch," or "Project Pacifica," or something like that? Nothing like that for us—too allusive, too suggestive. And no minutes of our meetings—too inhibiting. . . . About who might be reading them. Of course, we took notes for our own use. And among ourselves, we usually called ourselves "The Iron

Mountain Boys," or "Our Thing," or whatever came to mind. . . .

What can you tell me about the members of the Group?

I'll have to stick to generalities. . . . There were fifteen of us. The important thing was that we represented a very wide range of disciplines. And not all academic. People from the natural sciences, the social sciences, even the humanities. We had a lawyer and a businessman. Also, a professional war planner. Also, you should know that everyone in the Group had done work of distinction in at least two different fields. The interdisciplinary element was built in. . . .

It's true that there were no women in the Group, but I don't think that was significant. . . . We were all American citizens, of course. And all, I can say, in very good health, at least when we began. . . . You see, the first order of business, at the first meeting, was the reading of dossiers. They were very detailed, and not just professional, but also personal. They included medical histories. I remember one very curious thing, for whatever it's worth. Most of us, and that includes me, had a record of abnormally high uric acid concentrations in the blood. . . . None of us had ever had this experience, of a public inspection of credentials, or medical reports. It was very disturbing. . . .

But it was deliberate. The reason for it was to emphasize that we were supposed to make *all* our own decisions on procedure, without outside rules. This included judging each other's qualifications and making allowances for possible bias. I don't think it affected our work directly, but it made the point it was supposed to make. . . . That we should ignore absolutely nothing that might conceivably affect our objectivity.

[At this point I persuaded Doe that a brief occupational description of the individual members of the Group would serve a useful purpose for readers of the Report. The list which follows was worked out on paper. (It might be more accurate to say it was negotiated.) The problem was to give as much relevant information as possible without violating Doe's commitment to protect his colleagues' anonymity. It turned out to be very difficult, especially in the cases of those members who are very well known. For this reason, secondary areas of achievement or reputation are usually not shown.

The simple alphabetical "names" were assigned by Doe for convenient reference; they bear no intended relation to actual names. "Able" was the Group's Washington contact. It was he who brought and read the dossiers, and who most often acted as chairman. He, "Baker," and "Cox" were the three who had been involved in the preliminary planning. There is no other significance to the order of listing.

"Arthus Able" is an historian and political theorist, who has served in government.

"Bernard Baker" is a professor of international law and a consultant on government operations.

"Charles Cox" is an economist, social critic, and biographer.

"John Doe."

"Edward Ellis" is a sociologist often involved in public affairs.

"Frank Fox" is a cultural anthropologist.

"George Green" is a psychologist, educator, and developer of personnel testing systems.

"Harold Hill" is a psychiatrist, who has conducted extensive studies of the relationship between individual and group behavior.

"John Jones" is a scholar and literary critic.

"Martin Miller" is a physical chemist, whose work has received international recognition at the highest level.

"Paul Peters" is a biochemist, who has made important discoveries bearing on reproductive processes.

"Richard Roe" is a mathematician affiliated with an independent West Coast research institution.

"Samuel Smith" is an astronomer, physicist, and communications theorist.

"Thomas Taylor" is a systems analyst and war planner, who has written extensively on war, peace, and international relations.

"William White" is an industrialist, who has undertaken many special government assignments.]

How did the Group operate? I mean, where and when did you meet, and so forth?

We met on the average of once a month. Usually it was on weekends, and usually for two days. We had a few longer sessions, and one that lasted only four hours. . . . We met all over the country, always at a different place, except for the first and last times, which were at Iron Mountain. It was like a traveling seminar. . . . Sometimes at hotels, sometimes at universities. Twice we met at summer camps, and once at a private estate, in Virginia. We used a business place in Pittsburgh, and another in Poughkeepsie [New York]. . . . We never met in Washington, or on government property anywhere. . . . Able would announce the times and places two meetings ahead. They were never changed. . . .

We didn't divide into subcommittees, or anything else that formal. But we all took individual assignments between meetings. A lot of it involved getting information from other people. . . . Among the fifteen of us, I don't think there was anybody in the academic or professional world we couldn't call on if we wanted to, and we took advantage of it. . . . We were paid a very modest per diem. All of it was called "expenses" on the vouchers. We were told not to report it on our tax returns. . . . The checks were drawn on a special account of Able's at a New York bank. He signed them. . . . I don't know what the study cost. So far as our time and travel were concerned, it couldn't have come to more than the low six-figure range. But the big item must have been computer time, and I have no idea how high this ran. . . .

You say that you don't think your work was affected by professional bias. What about political and philosophical bias? Is it possible to deal with questions of war and peace without reflecting personal values?

Yes, it is. I can understand your skepticism. But if you had been at any of our meetings you'd have had a very hard time figuring out who were the liberals and who were the conservatives, or who were hawks and who were doves. There *is* such a thing as objectivity, and I think we had it. . . . I don't say no one had any emotional reaction to what we were doing. We all did, to some extent. As a matter of fact, two members had heart attacks after we were finished, and I'll be the first to admit it probably wasn't a coincidence.

You said you made your own ground rules. What were these ground rules?

The most important were informality and unanimity. By informality I mean that our discussions were open-ended. We went as far afield as any one of us thought we had to. For instance, we spent a lot of time on the relationship between military recruitment policies and industrial employment. Before we were finished with it, we'd gone through the history of western penal codes and any number of comparative psychiatric studies [of draftees and volunteers]. We looked over the organization of the Inca empire. We determined the effects of automation on underdeveloped societies. . . . It was all relevant. . . .

By unanimity, I don't mean that we kept taking votes, like a jury. I mean that we stayed with every issue until we had what the Quakers call a "sense of the meeting." It was time-consuming. But in the long run it saved time. Eventually we all got on the same wavelength, so to speak. . . .

Of course we had differences, and big ones, especially in the beginning. . . . For instance, in Section 1 you might think we were merely clarifying our instructions. Not so; it took a long time before we all agreed to a strict interpretation. . . . Roe and Taylor deserve most of the credit for this. . . . There are many things in the Report that look obvious now, but didn't seem so obvious then. For instance, on the relationship of war to social systems. The original premise was conventional, from Clausewitz. . . . That war was an "instrument" of broader political values. Able was the only one who challenged this, at first. Fox called his position "perverse." Yet it was Fox who furnished most of the data that led us all to agree with Able eventually. I mention this because I think it's a good example of the way we worked. A triumph of method over cliché. . . . I certainly don't intend to go into details about who took what side about what, and when. But I will say, to give credit where due, that only Roe, Able, Hill, and Taylor were able to see, at the beginning, where our method was taking us.

But you always reached agreement, eventually.

Yes. It's a unanimous report. . . . I don't mean that our sessions were always harmonious. Some of them were rough. The last six months there was a lot of quibbling about small points. . . . We'd been under pressure for a long time, we'd been working together too long. It was natural . . . that we got on each other's nerves. For a while Able and Taylor weren't speaking to each other. Miller threatened to quit. But this all passed. There were no important differences. . . .

*How was the Report actually written? Who
did the writing?*

We all had a hand in the first draft. Jones and Able put it together, and then mailed it around for review before working out a final version. . . . The only problems were the form it should take and whom we were writing it for. And, of course, the question of disclosure. . . . [Doe's comments on this point are summarized in the introduction.]

You mentioned a "peace games" manual. What are peace games?

I wanted to say something about that. The Report barely mentions it. "Peace games" is a method we developed during the course of the study. It's a forecasting technique, an information system. I'm very excited about it. Even if nothing is done about our recommendations—which is conceivable—this is something that can't be ignored. It will revolutionize the study of social problems. It's a by-product of the study. We needed a fast, dependable procedure to approximate the effects of disparate social phenomena on other social phenomena. We got it. It's in a primitive phase, but it works.

How are peace games played? Are they like Rand's war games?

You don't "play" peace games, like chess or Monopoly, any more than you play war games with toy soldiers. You use computers. It's a programming system. A computer "language," like Fortran, or Algol, or Jovial. . . . Its advantage is its superior capacity to interrelate data with no apparent common points of reference. . . . A simple analogy is likely to be misleading. But I can give you some examples. For instance, supposing I asked you to figure out what effect a moon landing by U.S. astronauts would have on an election in, say, Sweden. Or what effect a change in the draft law—a specific change—would have on the value of real estate in downtown Manhattan? Or a certain change in college entrance requirements in the United States on the British shipping industry?

You would probably say, first, that there would be no effect to speak of, and second, that there would be no way of telling. But you'd be wrong on both counts. In each case there would be an effect, and the peace games method could tell you what it would be, quantitatively. I didn't take these examples out of the air. We used them in working out the method. . . . Essentially, it's an elaborate high-speed trial-and-error system for determining working algorithms. Like most sophisticated types of computer problem-solving. . . .

A lot of the "games" of this kind you read about are just glorified conversational exercises. They really are games, and nothing more. I just saw one reported in the Canadian Computer Society Bulletin, called a "Vietnam Peace Game." They use simulation techniques, but the programming hypotheses are speculative. . . .

The idea of a problem-solving system like this is not original with us. ARPA[4] has been working on something like it. So has General Electric, in California. There are

[4] The Advanced Research Projects Agency, of the Department of Defense.

others. . . . We were successful not because we know more than they do about programming, which we don't, but because we learned how to formulate the problems accurately. It goes back to the old saw. You can always find the answer if you know the right question. . . .

Supposing you hadn't developed this method. Would you have come to the same conclusions in the Report?
Certainly. But it would have taken many times longer. . . . But please don't misunderstand my enthusiasm [about the peace games method]. With all due respect to the effects of computer technology on modern thinking, basic judgments must still be made by human beings. The peace games technique isn't responsible for our Report. We are. . . .

STATEMENT BY "JOHN DOE"

CONTRARY to the decision of the Special Study Group, of which I was a member, I have arranged for the general release of our Report. I am grateful to Mr. Leonard C. Lewin for his invaluable assistance in making this possible, and to The Dial Press for accepting the challenge of publication. Responsibility for taking this step, however, is mine and mine alone.

I am well aware that my action may be taken as a breach of faith by some of my former colleagues. But in my view my responsibility to the society of which I am a part supersedes any self-assumed obligation on the part of fifteen individual men. Since our Report can be considered on its merits, it is not necessary for me to disclose their identity to accomplish my purpose. Yet I would gladly abandon my own anonymity if it were possible to do so without at the same time compromising theirs, to defend our work publicly if and when they release me from this personal bond.

But this is secondary. What is needed now, and needed badly, is widespread public discussion and debate about the elements of war and the problems of peace. I hope that publication of this Report will serve to initiate it.

THE REPORT OF
THE SPECIAL STUDY GROUP

LETTER OF TRANSMITTAL

To the convener of this group:

Attached is the Report of the Special Study Group established by you in August, 1963, 1) to consider the problems involved in the contingency of a transition to a general condition of peace, and 2) to recommend procedures for dealing with this contingency. For the convenience of nontechnical readers we have elected to submit our statistical supporting data, totaling 604 exhibits, separately, as well as a preliminary manual of the "peace games" method devised during the course of our study.

We have completed our assignment to the best of our ability, subject to the limitations of time and resources available to us. Our conclusions of fact and our recommendations are unanimous; those of us who differ in certain secondary respects from the findings set forth herein do not consider these differences sufficient to warrant the filing of a minority report. It is our earnest hope that the fruits of our deliberations will be of value to our government in its efforts to provide leadership to the nation in solving the complex and far-reaching problems we have examined, and that our recommendations for subsequent Presidential action in this area will be adopted.

Because of the unusual circumstances surrounding the establishment of this Group, and in view of the nature of its findings, we do not recommend that this Report be released for publication. It is our affirmative judgment that such action would not be in the public interest. The uncertain advantages of public discussion of our conclusions and recommendations are, in our opinion, greatly outweighed by the clear and predictable danger of a crisis in public confidence which untimely publication of this Report might be expected to provoke. The likelihood that a lay reader, unexposed to the exigencies of higher political or military responsibility, will misconstrue the purpose of this project, and the intent of its participants, seems obvious. We urge that circulation of this Report be closely restricted to those whose responsibilities require that they be apprised of its contents.

We deeply regret that the necessity of anonymity, a prerequisite to our Group's unhindered pursuit of its objectives, precludes proper acknowledgment of our gratitude to the many persons in and out of government who contributed so greatly to our work.

For the Special Study Group
[*signature withheld for publication*]

30 September, 1966

INTRODUCTION

THE REPORT which follows summarizes the results of a
two-and-a-half-year study of the broad problems to be
anticipated in the event of a general transformation of
American society to a condition lacking its most critical
current characteristics: its capability and readiness to
make war when doing so is judged necessary or desirable by its political leadership.

Our work has been predicated on the belief that
some kind of general peace may soon be negotiable. The
de facto admission of Communist China into the United
Nations now appears to be only a few years away at
most. It has become increasingly manifest that conflicts
of American national interest with those of China and
the Soviet Union are susceptible of political solution,

despite the superficial contraindications of the current Vietnam war, of the threats of an attack on China, and of the necessarily hostile tenor of day-to-day foreign policy statements. It is also obvious that differences involving other nations can be readily resolved by the three great powers whenever they arrive at a stable peace among themselves. It is not necessary, for the purposes of our study, to assume that a general détente of this sort *will* come about—and we make no such argument—but only that it *may*.

It is surely no exaggeration to say that a condition of general world peace would lead to changes in the social structures of the nations of the world of unparalleled and revolutionary magnitude. The economic impact of general disarmament, to name only the most obvious consequence of peace, would revise the production and distribution patterns of the globe to a degree that would make the changes of the past fifty years seem insignificant. Political, sociological, cultural, and ecological changes would be equally far-reaching. What has motivated our study of these contingencies has been the growing sense of thoughtful men in and out of government that the world is totally unprepared to meet the demands of such a situation.

We had originally planned, when our study was initiated, to address ourselves to these two broad questions and their components: *What can be expected if peace comes? What should we be prepared to do about it?* But as our investigation proceeded it became apparent that certain other questions had to be faced.

What, for instance, are the real functions of war in modern societies, beyond the ostensible ones of defending and advancing the "national interests" of nations? In the absence of war, what other institutions exist or might be devised to fulfill these functions? Granting that a "peaceful" settlement of disputes is within the range of current international relationships, is the abolition of war, in the broad sense, really possible? If so, is it necessarily desirable, in terms of social stability? If not, what can be done to improve the operation of our social system in respect to its war-readiness?

The word *peace*, as we have used it in the following pages, describes a permanent, or quasi-permanent, condition entirely free from the national exercise, or contemplation, of any form of the organized social violence, or threat of violence, generally known as war. It implies total and general disarmament. It is not used to describe the more familiar condition of "cold war," "armed peace," or other mere respite, long or short, from armed conflict. Nor is it used simply as a synonym for the political settlement of international differences. The magnitude of modern means of mass destruction and the speed of modern communications require the unqualified working definition given above; only a generation ago such an absolute description would have seemed utopian rather than pragmatic. Today, any modification of this definition would render it almost worthless for our purpose. By the same standard, we have used the word *war* to apply interchangeably to conventional ("hot") war, to the general condition of war preparation or war readiness, and

to the general "war system." The sense intended is made
clear in context.

The first section of our Report deals with its scope
and with the assumptions on which our study was based.
The second considers the effects of disarmament on the
economy, the subject of most peace research to date. The
third takes up so-called "disarmament scenarios" which
have been proposed. The fourth, fifth, and sixth examine
the nonmilitary functions of war and the problems they
raise for a viable transition to peace; here will be found
some indications of the true dimensions of the problem,
not previously coordinated in any other study. In the
seventh section we summarize our findings, and in the
eighth we set forth our recommendations for what we
believe to be a practical and necessary course of action.

SECTION 1

SCOPE OF THE STUDY

WHEN THE SPECIAL STUDY GROUP was established in August, 1963, its members were instructed to govern their deliberations in accordance with three principal criteria. Briefly stated, they were these: 1) military-style objectivity; 2) avoidance of preconceived value assumptions; 3) inclusion of all relevant areas of theory and data.

These guideposts are by no means as obvious as they may appear at first glance, and we believe it necessary to indicate clearly how they were to inform our work. For they express succinctly the limitations of previous "peace studies," and imply the nature of both government and unofficial dissatisfaction with these earlier efforts. It is not our intention here to minimize the significance of the work of our predecessors, or to belittle the quality of their contributions. What we have tried to do, and believe we have done, is extend their scope. We hope that our conclusions may serve in turn as a starting point for still broader and more detailed examinations of every aspect of the problems of transition to peace and of the questions which must be answered before such a transition can be allowed to get under way.

It is a truism that objectivity is more often an intention expressed than an attitude achieved, but the intention—conscious, unambiguous, and constantly self-critical —is a precondition to its achievement. We believe it no accident that we were charged to use a "military contingency" model for our study, and we owe a considerable debt to the civilian war planning agencies for their pioneering work in the objective examination of the contingencies of nuclear war. There is no such precedent in peace studies. Much of the usefulness of even the most elaborate and carefully reasoned programs for economic conversion to peace, for example, has been vitiated by a wishful eagerness to demonstrate that peace is not only possible, but even cheap or easy. One official report is replete with references to the critical role of "dynamic optimism" on economic developments, and goes on to submit, as evidence, that it "would be hard to imagine that the American people would not respond very positively to an agreed and safeguarded program to substitute an international rule of law and order," etc.[1] Another line of argument frequently taken is that disarmament would entail comparatively little disruption of the economy, since it need only be partial; we will deal with this approach later. Yet genuine objectivity in war studies is often criticized as inhuman. As Herman Kahn, the writer on strategic studies best known to the general public, put it: "Critics frequently object to the icy rationality of the Hudson Institute, the Rand Corporation, and other such organizations. I'm always tempted to ask in reply, 'Would you prefer a warm, human error? Do you feel better with a nice emotional mistake?' "[2] And, as Secretary of Defense Robert S. McNamara has pointed out, in reference to facing up to the possibility of nuclear war, "Some people are afraid even to look over the edge. But in a thermonuclear war we cannot afford any political acrophobia."[3] Surely it should be self-evident that this applies equally to the opposite prospect, but so far no one has taken more than a timid glance over the brink of peace.

An intention to avoid preconceived value judgments is if anything even more productive of self-delusion. We claim no immunity, as individuals, from this type of bias, but we have made a continuously self-conscious effort to deal with the problems of peace without, for example, considering that a condition of peace is *per se* "good" or "bad." This has not been easy, but it has been obligatory; to our knowledge, it has not been done before. Previous studies have taken the desirability of peace, the importance of human life, the superiority of democratic institutions, the greatest "good" for the greatest number, the "dignity" of the individual, the desirability of maximum health and longevity, and other such wishful premises as axiomatic values necessary for the justification of a study of peace issues. We have not found them so. We have attempted to apply the standards of physical science to our thinking, the principal characteristic of which is not quantification, as is popularly believed, but that, in Whitehead's words, ". . . it ignores all judgments of value; for instance, all esthetic and moral judgments."[4] Yet it is obvious that any serious investigation of a problem, however "pure," must be informed by some normative standard. In this case it has been simply the survival of human society in general, of American society in particular, and, as a corollary to survival, the stability of this society.

It is interesting, we believe, to note that the most dispassionate planners of nuclear strategy also recognize that the stability of society is the one bedrock value that *cannot* be avoided. Secretary McNamara has defended the need for American nuclear superiority on the grounds that it "makes possible a strategy designed to preserve the fabric of our societies if war should occur."[5] A former member of the Department of State policy planning staff goes further. "A more precise word for peace, in terms of the practical world, is stability. . . . Today the great nuclear panoplies are essential elements in such stability as exists. Our present purpose must be to continue the process of learning how to live with them."[6] We, of course, do not equate stability with peace, but we accept it as the one common assumed objective of both peace and war.

The third criterion—breadth—has taken us still farther afield from peace studies made to date. It is obvious to any layman that the economic patterns of a warless world will be drastically different from those we live with today, and it is equally obvious that the political relationships of nations will not be those we have learned to take for granted, sometimes described as a global version of the adversary system of our common law. But the social implications of peace extend far beyond its putative effects on national economies and international relations. As we shall show, the relevance of peace and war to the internal political organization of societies, to the sociological relationships of their members, to psychological motivations, to ecological processes, and to cultural values is equally profound. More important, it is equally critical in assaying the consequences of a transition to peace, and in determining the feasibility of any transition at all.

It is not surprising that these less obvious factors have been generally ignored in peace research. They have not lent themselves to systematic analysis. They have been difficult, perhaps impossible, to measure with any degree of assurance that estimates of their effects could be depended on. They are "intangibles," but only in the sense that abstract concepts in mathematics are intangible compared to those which can be quantified. Economic factors, on the other hand, can be measured, at least superficially; and international relationships can be verbalized, like law, into logical sequences.

We do not claim that we have discovered an infallible way of measuring these other factors, or of assigning them precise weights in the equation of transition. But we believe we have taken their relative importance into account to this extent: we have removed them from the category of the "intangible," hence scientifically suspect and therefore somehow of secondary importance, and brought them out into the realm of the objective. The result, we believe, provides a context of realism for the discussion of the issues relating to the possible transition to peace which up to now has been missing.

This is not to say that we presume to have found the answers we were seeking. But we believe that our emphasis on breadth of scope has made it at least possible to begin to understand the questions.

SECTION 2

DISARMAMENT AND
THE ECONOMY

IN THIS SECTION we shall briefly examine some of the common features of the studies that have been published dealing with one or another aspect of the expected impact of disarmament on the American economy. Whether disarmament is considered as a by-product of peace or as its precondition, its effect on the national economy will in either case be the most immediately felt of its consequences. The quasi-mensurable quality of economic manifestations has given rise to more detailed speculation in this area than in any other.

General agreement prevails in respect to the more important economic problems that general disarmament would raise. A short survey of these problems, rather than a detailed critique of their comparative significance, is sufficient for our purposes in this Report.

The first factor is that of size. The "world war industry," as one writer[1] has aptly called it, accounts for approximately a tenth of the output of the world's total economy. Although this figure is subject to fluctuation, the causes of which are themselves subject to regional variation, it tends to hold fairly steady. The United States, as the world's richest nation, not only accounts for the largest single share of this expense, currently upward of $60 billion a year, but also ". . . has devoted a higher *proportion* [emphasis added] of its gross national product to its military establishment than any other major free world nation. This was true even before our increased expenditures in Southeast Asia."[2] Plans for economic conversion that minimize the economic magnitude of the problem do so only by rationalizing, however persuasively, the maintenance of a substantial residual military budget under some euphemized classification.

Conversion of military expenditures to other purposes entails a number of difficulties. The most serious stems from the degree of rigid specialization that characterizes modern war production, best exemplified in nuclear and missile technology. This constituted no fundamental problem after World War II, nor did the question of free-market consumer demand for "conventional" items of consumption—those goods and services consumers had already been conditioned to require. Today's situation is qualitatively different in both respects.

This inflexibility is geographical and occupational, as well as industrial, a fact which has led most analysts of the economic impact of disarmament to focus their attention on phased plans for the relocation of war industry personnel and capital installations as much as on proposals for developing new patterns of consumption. One serious flaw common to such plans is the kind called in the natural sciences the "macroscopic error." An implicit presumption is made that a total national plan for conversion differs from a community program to cope with the shutting down of a "defense facility" only in degree. We find no reason to believe that this is the case, nor that a general enlargement of such local programs, however well thought out in terms of housing, occupational retraining, and the like, can be applied on a national scale. A national economy can absorb almost any number of subsidiary reorganizations within its total limits, providing there is no basic change in its own structure. General disarmament, which would require such basic changes, lends itself to no valid smaller-scale analogy.

Even more questionable are the models proposed for the retraining of labor for nonarmaments occupations. Putting aside for the moment the unsolved questions dealing with the nature of new distribution patterns—retraining for what?—the increasingly specialized job skills associated with war industry production are further depreciated by the accelerating inroads of the industrial techniques loosely described as "automation." It is not too much to say that general disarmament would require the scrapping of a critical proportion of the most highly developed occupational specialties in the economy. The political difficulties inherent in such an "adjustment"

would make the outcries resulting from the closing of a
few obsolete military and naval installations in 1964
sound like a whisper.

In general, discussions of the problems of conversion
have been characterized by an unwillingness to recognize
its special quality. This is best exemplified by the 1965
report of the Ackley Committee.[3] One critic has tellingly
pointed out that it blindly assumes that ". . . nothing in
the arms economy—neither its size, nor its geographical
concentration, nor its highly specialized nature, nor the
peculiarities of its market, nor the special nature of much
of its labor force—endows it with any uniqueness when
the necessary time of adjustment comes."[4]

Let us assume, however, despite the lack of evidence
that a viable program for conversion can be developed in
the framework of the existing economy, that the problems
noted above can be solved. What proposals have been
offered for utilizing the productive capabilities that disarmament would presumably release?

The most commonly held theory is simply that general
economic reinvestment would absorb the greater part of
these capabilities. Even though it is now largely taken
for granted (and even by today's equivalent of traditional laissez-faire economists) that unprecedented government assistance (and concomitant government control) will be needed to solve the "structural" problems
of transition, a general attitude of confidence prevails
that new consumption patterns will take up the slack.
What is less clear is the nature of these patterns.

One school of economists has it that these patterns

will develop on their own. It envisages the equivalent of the arms budget being returned, under careful control, to the consumer, in the form of tax cuts. Another, recognizing the undeniable need for increased "consumption" in what is generally considered the public sector of the economy, stresses vastly increased government spending in such areas of national concern as health, education, mass transportation, low-cost housing, water supply, control of the physical environment, and, stated generally, "poverty."

The mechanisms proposed for controlling the transition to an arms-free economy are also traditional— changes in both sides of the federal budget, manipulation of interest rates, etc. We acknowledge the undeniable value of fiscal tools in a normal cyclical economy, where they provide leverage to accelerate or brake an existing trend. Their more committed proponents, however, tend to lose sight of the fact that there is a limit to the power of these devices to influence fundamental economic forces. They can provide new incentives in the economy, but they cannot in themselves transform the production of a billion dollars' worth of missiles a year to the equivalent in food, clothing, prefabricated houses, or television sets. At bottom, they reflect the economy; they do not motivate it.

More sophisticated, and less sanguine, analysts contemplate the diversion of the arms budget to a nonmilitary system equally remote from the market economy. What the "pyramid-builders" frequently suggest is the expansion of space-research programs to the dollar level of current armaments expenditures. This approach has the superficial merit of reducing the size of the problem of transferability of resources, but introduces other difficulties, which we will take up in section 6.

Without singling out any one of the several major studies of the expected impact of disarmament on the economy for special criticism, we can summarize our objections to them in general terms as follows:

1. No proposed program for economic conversion to disarmament sufficiently takes into account the unique magnitude of the required adjustments it would entail.

2. Proposals to transform arms production into a beneficent scheme of public works are more the products of wishful thinking than of realistic understanding of the limits of our existing economic system.

3. Fiscal and monetary measures are inadequate as controls for the process of transition to an arms-free economy.

4. Insufficient attention has been paid to the political acceptability of the objectives of the proposed conversion models, as well as of the political means to be employed in effectuating a transition.

5. No serious consideration has been given, in any proposed conversion plan, to the fundamental nonmilitary function of war and armaments in modern society, nor has any explicit attempt been made to devise a viable substitute for it. This criticism will be developed in sections 5 and 6.

SECTION 3

DISARMAMENT SCENARIOS

Scenarios, as they have come to be called, are hypothetical constructions of future events. Inevitably, they are composed of varying proportions of established fact, reasonable inference, and more or less inspired guesswork. Those which have been suggested as model procedures for effectuating international arms control and eventual disarmament are necessarily imaginative, although closely reasoned; in this respect they resemble the "war games" analyses of the Rand Corporation, with which they share a common conceptual origin.

All such scenarios that have been seriously put forth imply a dependence on bilateral or multilateral agreement between the great powers. In general, they call for a progressive phasing out of gross armaments, military forces, weapons, and weapons technology, coordinated with elaborate matching procedures of verification, inspection, and machinery for the settlement of international disputes. It should be noted that even proponents of unilateral disarmament qualify their proposals with an implied requirement of reciprocity, very much in the manner of a scenario of graduated response in nuclear war. The advantage of unilateral initiative lies in its political value as an expression of good faith, as well as in its diplomatic function as a catalyst for formal disarmament negotiations.

The READ model for disarmament (developed by the Research Program on Economic Adjustments to Disarmament) is typical of these scenarios. It is a twelve-year-program, divided into three-year stages. Each stage includes a separate phase of: reduction of armed forces; cutbacks of weapons production, inventories, and foreign military bases; development of international inspection procedures and control conventions; and the building up of a sovereign international disarmament organization. It anticipates a net matching decline in U.S. defense expenditures of only somewhat more than half the 1965 level, but a necessary redeployment of some five-sixths of the defense-dependent labor force.

The economic implications assigned by their authors to various disarmament scenarios diverge widely. The more conservative models, like that cited above, emphasize economic as well as military prudence in postulating eiaborate fail-safe disarmament agencies, which themselves require expenditures substantially substituting for those of the displaced war industries. Such programs stress the advantages of the smaller economic adjustment entailed.[1] Others emphasize, on the contrary, the magnitude (and the opposite advantages) of the savings to be achieved from disarmament. One widely read analysis[2] estimates the annual cost of the inspection function of general disarmament throughout the world as only between two and three percent of current military expenditures. Both types of plan tend to deal with the anticipated problem of economic reinvestment only in the aggregate. We have seen no proposed disarmament sequence that correlates the phasing out of specific kinds of military spending with specific new forms of substitute spending.

Without examining disarmament scenarios in greater detail, we may characterize them with these general comments:

1. Given genuine agreement of intent among the great powers, the scheduling of arms control and elimination presents no inherently insurmountable procedural problems. Any of several proposed sequences might serve as the basis for multilateral agreement or for the first step in unilateral arms reduction.

2. No major power can proceed with such a program, however, until it has developed an economic conversion plan fully integrated with each phase of disarmament. No such plan has yet been developed in the United States.

3. Furthermore, disarmament scenarios, like proposals for economic conversion, make no allowance for the nonmilitary functions of war in modern societies, and offer no surrogate for these necessary functions. One partial exception is a proposal for the "unarmed forces of the United States," which we will consider in section 6.

SECTION 4

WAR AND PEACE
AS SOCIAL SYSTEMS

WE HAVE DEALT only sketchily with proposed disarmament scenarios and economic analyses, but the reason
for our seemingly casual dismissal of so much serious
and sophisticated work lies in no disrespect for its com-
petence. It is rather a question of relevance. To put it
plainly, all these programs, however detailed and well
developed, are abstractions. The most carefully reasoned
disarmament sequence inevitably reads more like the
rules of a game or a classroom exercise in logic than like
a prognosis of real events in the real world. This is as
true of today's complex proposals as it was of the Abbé
de St. Pierre's "Plan for Perpetual Peace in Europe" 250
years ago.

Some essential element has clearly been lacking in

all these schemes. One of our first tasks was to try to bring this missing quality into definable focus, and we believe we have succeeded in doing so. We find that at the heart of every peace study we have examined—from the modest technological proposal (e.g., to convert a poison gas plant to the production of "socially useful" equivalents) to the most elaborate scenario for universal peace in our time—lies one common fundamental misconception. It is the source of the miasma of unreality surrounding such plans. *It is the incorrect assumption that war, as an institution, is subordinate to the social systems it is believed to serve.*

This misconception, although profound and far-reaching, is entirely comprehensible. Few social clichés are so unquestioningly accepted as the notion that war is an extension of diplomacy (or of politics, or of the pursuit of economic objectives). If this were true, it would be wholly appropriate for economists and political theorists to look on the problems of transition to peace as essentially mechanical or procedural—as indeed they do, treating them as logistic corollaries of the settlement of national conflicts of interest. If this were true, there would be no real substance to the difficulties of transition. For it is evident that even in today's world there exists no conceivable conflict of interest, real or imaginary, between nations or between social forces within nations, that cannot be resolved without recourse to war—*if* such resolution were assigned a priority of social value. And if this were true, the economic analyses and disarmament proposals we have referred to, plausible and well conceived as they may be, would not inspire, as they do, an inescapable sense of indirection.

The point is that the cliché is not true, and the problems of transition are indeed substantive rather than merely procedural. Although war is "used" as an instrument of national and social policy, the fact that a society is organized for any degree of readiness for war supersedes its political and economic structure. War itself is the basic social system, within which other secondary modes of social organization conflict or conspire. It is the system which has governed most human societies of record, as it is today.

Once this is correctly understood, the true magnitude of the problems entailed in a transition to peace—itself a social system, but without precedent except in a few simple preindustrial societies—becomes apparent. At the same time, some of the puzzling superficial contradictions of modern societies can then be readily rationalized. The "unnecessary" size and power of the world war industry; the preeminence of the military establishment in every society, whether open or concealed; the exemption of military or paramilitary institutions from the accepted social and legal standards of behavior required elsewhere in the society; the successful operation of the armed forces and the armaments producers entirely outside the framework of each nation's economic ground rules: these and other ambiguities closely associated with the relationship of war to society are easily clarified, once the priority of war-making potential as the principal structuring force in society is accepted. Economic systems, political philosophies, and corpora jures serve and extend the war system, not vice versa.

It must be emphasized that the precedence of a society's war-making potential over its other characteristics is not the result of the "threat" presumed to exist at any one time from other societies. This is the reverse of the basic situation; "threats" against the "national interest" are usually created or accelerated to meet the changing needs of the war system. Only in comparatively recent times has it been considered politically expedient to euphemize war budgets as "defense" requirements. The necessity for governments to distinguish between "aggression" (bad) and "defense" (good) has been a by-product of rising literacy and rapid communication. The distinction is tactical only, a concession to the growing inadequacy of ancient war-organizing political rationales.

Wars are not "caused" by international conflicts of interest. Proper logical sequence would make it more often accurate to say that war-making societies require— and thus bring about—such conflicts. The capacity of a nation to make war expresses the greatest social power it can exercise; war-making, active or contemplated, is a matter of life and death on the greatest scale subject to social control. It should therefore hardly be surprising that the military institutions in each society claim its highest priorities.

We find further that most of the confusion surrounding the myth that war-making is a tool of state policy stems from a general misapprehension of the functions of war. In general, these are conceived as: to defend a nation from military attack by another, or to deter such an attack; to defend or advance a "national interest"— economic, political, ideological; to maintain or increase a nation's military power for its own sake. These are the visible, or ostensible, functions of war. If there were no others, the importance of the war establishment in each society might in fact decline to the subordinate level it is believed to occupy. And the elimination of war would indeed be the procedural matter that the disarmament scenarios suggest.

But there are other, broader, more profoundly felt functions of war in modern societies. It is these invisible, or implied, functions that maintain war-readiness as the dominant force in our societies. And it is the unwillingness or inability of the writers of disarmament scenarios and reconversion plans to take them into account that has so reduced the usefulness of their work, and that has made it seem unrelated to the world we know.

SECTION 5

THE FUNCTIONS OF WAR

As we have indicated, the preeminence of the concept of war as the principal organizing force in most societies has been insufficiently appreciated. This is also true of its extensive effects throughout the many nonmilitary activities of society. These effects are less apparent in complex industrial societies like our own than in primitive cultures, the activities of which can be more easily and fully comprehended.

We propose in this section to examine these nonmilitary, implied, and usually invisible functions of war, to the extent that they bear on the problems of transition to peace for our society. The military, or ostensible, function of the war system requires no elaboration; it serves simply to defend or advance the "national interest" by means of organized violence. It is often necessary for a national military establishment to create a need for its unique powers—to maintain the franchise, so to speak. And a healthy military apparatus requires regular "exercise," by whatever rationale seems expedient, to prevent its atrophy.

The nonmilitary functions of the war system are more basic. They exist not merely to justify themselves but to serve broader social purposes. If and when war is eliminated, the military functions it has served will end with it. But its nonmilitary functions will not. It is essential, therefore, that we understand their significance before we can reasonably expect to evaluate whatever institutions may be proposed to replace them.

Economic

The production of weapons of mass destruction has always been associated with economic "waste." The term is pejorative, since it implies a failure of function. But no human activity can properly be considered wasteful if it achieves its contextual objective. The phrase "wasteful but necessary," applied not only to war expenditures but to most of the "unproductive" commercial activities of our society, is a contradiction in terms. ". . . The attacks that have since the time of Samuel's criticism of King Saul been leveled against military expenditures as waste may well have concealed or misunderstood the point that some kinds of waste may have a larger social utility."[1]

In the case of military "waste," there is indeed a larger social utility. It derives from the fact that the "wastefulness" of war production is exercised entirely outside the framework of the economy of supply and demand. As such, it provides the only critically large segment of the total economy that is subject to complete and arbitrary central control. If modern industrial societies can be defined as those which have developed the capacity to produce more than is required for their economic survival (regardless of the equities of distribution of goods within them), military spending can be said to furnish the only balance wheel with sufficient inertia to stabilize the advance of their economies. The fact that war is "wasteful" is what enables it to serve this function. And the faster the economy advances, the heavier this balance wheel must be.

This function is often viewed, oversimply, as a device for the control of surpluses. One writer on the subject puts it this way: "Why is war so wonderful? Because it creates artificial demand . . . the only kind of artificial demand, moreover, that does not raise any political issues: *war, and only war, solves the problem of inventory.*"[2] The reference here is to shooting war, but it applies equally to the general war economy as well. "It is generally agreed," concludes, more cautiously, the report of a panel set up by the U.S. Arms Control and Disarmament Agency, "that the greatly expanded public sector since World War II, resulting from heavy defense expenditures, has provided additional protection against depressions, since this sector is not responsive to contraction in the private sector and has provided a sort of buffer or balance wheel in the economy."[3]

The *principal* economic function of war, in our view, is that it provides just such a flywheel. It is not to be confused in function with the various forms of fiscal control, none of which directly engages vast numbers of men and units of production. It is not to be confused with massive government expenditures in social welfare programs; once initiated, such programs normally become integral parts of the general economy and are no longer subject to arbitrary control.

But even in the context of the general civilian economy war cannot be considered wholly "wasteful." Without a long-established war economy, and without its frequent eruption into large-scale shooting war, most of the major industrial advances known to history, beginning with the development of iron, could never have taken place. Weapons technology structures the economy. According to the writer cited above, "Nothing is more ironic or revealing about our society than the fact that hugely destructive war is a very progressive force in it. . . . War production is progressive because it is production that would not otherwise have taken place. (It is not so widely appreciated, for example, that the civilian standard of living *rose* during World War II.)"[4] This is not "ironic or revealing," but essentially a simple statement of fact.

It should also be noted that war production has a dependably stimulating effect outside itself. Far from constituting a "wasteful" drain on the economy, war spending, considered pragmatically, has been a consistently positive factor in the rise of gross national product and of individual productivity. A former Secretary of the Army has carefully phrased it for public consumption thus: "If there is, as I suspect there is, a direct relation between the stimulus of large defense spending and a substantially increased rate of growth of gross national product, it quite simply follows that defense spending *per se* might be countenanced *on economic grounds alone* [emphasis added] as a stimulator of the national metabolism."[5] Actually, the fundamental nonmilitary utility of war in the economy is far more widely acknowledged than the scarcity of such affirmations as that quoted above would suggest.

But *negatively* phrased public recognitions of the importance of war to the general economy abound. The most familiar example is the effect of "peace threats" on the stock market, e.g., "Wall Street was shaken yesterday by news of an apparent peace feeler from North Vietnam, but swiftly recovered its composure after about an hour of sometimes indiscriminate selling."[6] Savings banks solicit deposits with similar cautionary slogans, e.g., "If peace breaks out, will you be ready for it?" A more subtle case in point was the recent refusal of the Department of Defense to permit the West German government to substitute nonmilitary goods for unwanted armaments in its purchase commitments from the United States; the decisive consideration was that the German purchases should not affect the general (nonmilitary) economy. Other incidental examples are to be found in the pressures brought to bear on the Department when it announces plans to close down an obsolete facility (as a "wasteful" form of "waste"), and in the usual coordination of stepped-up military activities (as in Vietnam in 1965) with dangerously rising unemployment rates.

Although we do not imply that a substitute for war in the economy cannot be devised, no combination of techniques for controlling employment, production, and consumption has yet been tested that can remotely compare to it in effectiveness. It is, and has been, the essential economic stabilizer of modern societies.

Political

The political functions of war have been up to now even more critical to social stability. It is not surprising, nevertheless, that discussions of economic conversion for peace tend to fall silent on the matter of political implementation, and that disarmament scenarios, often sophisticated in their weighing of international political factors, tend to disregard the political functions of the war system within individual societies.

These functions are essentially organizational. First of all, the existence of a society as a political "nation" requires as part of its definition an attitude of relationship toward other "nations." This is what we usually call a foreign policy. But a nation's foreign policy can have no substance if it lacks the means of enforcing its attitude toward other nations. It can do this in a credible manner only if it implies the threat of maximum political organization for this purpose—which is to say that it is organized to some degree for war. War, then, as we have defined it to include all national activities that recognize the possibility of armed conflict, is itself the defining element of any nation's existence vis-à-vis any other nation. Since it is historically axiomatic that the existence of any form of weaponry insures its use, we have used the word "peace" as virtually synonymous with disarmament. By the same token, "war" is virtually synonymous with nationhood. The elimination of war implies the inevitable elimination of national sovereignty and the traditional nation-state.

The war system not only has been essential to the existence of nations as independent political entities, but has been equally indispensable to their stable internal political structure. Without it, no government has ever been able to obtain acquiescence in its "legitimacy," or right to rule its society. The possibility of war provides the sense of external necessity without which no government can long remain in power. The historical record reveals one instance after another where the failure of a regime to maintain the credibility of a war threat led to its dissolution, by the forces of private interest, of reactions to social injustice, or of other disintegrative elements. The organization of a society for the possibility of war is its principal political stabilizer. It is ironic that this primary function of war has been generally recognized by historians only where it has been expressly acknowledged—in the pirate societies of the great conquerors.

The basic authority of a modern state over its people resides in its war powers. (There is, in fact, good reason to believe that codified law had its origins in the rules of

conduct established by military victors for dealing with
the defeated enemy, which were later adapted to apply
to all subject populations.[7]) On a day-to-day basis, it
is represented by the institution of police, armed organizations charged expressly with dealing with "internal
enemies" in a military manner. Like the conventional "external" military, the police are also substantially exempt
from many civilian legal restraints on their social behavior. In some countries, the artificial distinction between
police and other military forces does not exist. On the
long-term basis, a government's emergency war powers
—inherent in the structure of even the most libertarian
of nations—define the most significant aspect of the relation between state and citizen.

In advanced modern democratic societies, the war
system has provided political leaders with another polit-
ical-economic function of increasing importance: it has
served as the last great safeguard against the elimination
of necessary social classes. As economic productivity in-
creases to a level further and further above that of minimum subsistence, it becomes more and more difficult for
a society to maintain distribution patterns insuring the
existence of "hewers of wood and drawers of water." The
further progress of automation can be expected to dif-
ferentiate still more sharply between "superior" workers
and what Ricardo called "menials," while simultaneously
aggravating the problem of maintaining an unskilled
labor supply.

The arbitrary nature of war expenditures and of other
military activities make them ideally suited to control

these essential class relationships. Obviously, if the war system were to be discarded, new political machinery would be needed at once to serve this vital subfunction. Until it is developed, the continuance of the war system must be assured, if for no other reason, among others, than to preserve whatever quality and degree of poverty a society requires as an incentive, as well as to maintain the stability of its internal organization of power.

Sociological

Under this heading, we will examine a nexus of functions served by the war system that affect human behavior in society. In general, they are broader in application and less susceptible to direct observation than the economic and political factors previously considered.

The most obvious of these functions is the time-honored use of military institutions to provide antisocial elements with an acceptable role in the social structure. The disintegrative, unstable social movements loosely described as "fascist" have traditionally taken root in societies that have lacked adequate military or paramilitary outlets to meet the needs of these elements. This function has been critical in periods of rapid change. The danger signals are easy to recognize, even though the stigmata bear different names at different times. The current euphemistic clichés—"juvenile delinquency" and "alienation"—have had their counterparts in every age. In earlier days these conditions were dealt with directly by the military without the complications of due process, usually through press gangs or outright enslavement. But

it is not hard to visualize, for example, the degree of
social disruption that might have taken place in the
United States during the last two decades if the problem of the socially disaffected of the post-World War II
period had not been foreseen and effectively met. The
younger, and more dangerous, of these hostile social
groupings have been kept under control by the Selective
Service System.

This system and its analogues elsewhere furnish remarkably clear examples of disguised military utility.
Informed persons in this country have never accepted
the official rationale for a peacetime draft—military necessity, preparedness, etc.—as worthy of serious consideration. But what has gained credence among thoughtful
men is the rarely voiced, less easily refuted, proposition
that the institution of military service has a "patriotic"
priority in our society that must be maintained for its
own sake. Ironically, the simplistic official justification for
selective service comes closer to the mark, once the nonmilitary functions of military institutions are understood.
As a control device over the hostile, nihilistic, and potentially unsettling elements of a society in transition,
the draft can again be defended, and quite convincingly,
as a "military" necessity.

Nor can it be considered a coincidence that overt
military activity, and thus the level of draft calls, tend to
follow the major fluctuations in the unemployment rate
in the lower age groups. This rate, in turn, is a time-
tested herald of social discontent. It must be noted also

that the armed forces in every civilization have provided
the principal state-supported haven for what we now
call the "unemployable." The typical European standing army (of fifty years ago) consisted of ". . . troops
unfit for employment in commerce, industry, or agricul-
ture, led by officers unfit to practice any legitimate pro-
fession or to conduct a business enterprise."[8] This is still
largely true, if less apparent. In a sense, this function of
the military as the custodian of the economically or
culturally deprived was the forerunner of most contemporary civilian social-welfare programs, from the
W.P.A. to various forms of "socialized" medicine and
social security. It is interesting that liberal sociologists
currently proposing to use the Selective Service System
as a medium of cultural upgrading of the poor consider
this a *novel* application of military practice.

Although it cannot be said absolutely that such critical
measures of social control as the draft require a military
rationale, no modern society has yet been willing to risk
experimentation with any other kind. Even during such
periods of comparatively simple social crisis as the so-
called Great Depression of the 1930s, it was deemed
prudent by the government to invest minor make-work
projects, like the "Civilian" Conservation Corps, with a
military character, and to place the more ambitious National Recovery Administration under the direction of
a professional army officer at its inception. Today, at
least one small Northern European country, plagued with
uncontrollable unrest among its "alienated youth," is con-

sidering the expansion of its armed forces, despite the problem of making credible the expansion of a non-existent external threat.

Sporadic efforts have been made to promote general recognition of broad national values free of military connotation, but they have been ineffective. For example, to enlist public support of even such modest programs of social adjustment as "fighting inflation" or "maintaining physical fitness" it has been necessary for the government to utilize a patriotic (i.e., military) incentive. It sells "defense" bonds and it equates health with military preparedness. This is not surprising; since the concept of "nationhood" implies readiness for war, a "national" program must do likewise.

In general, the war system provides the basic motivation for primary social organization. In so doing, it reflects on the societal level the incentives of individual human behavior. The most important of these, for social purposes, is the individual psychological rationale for allegiance to a society and its values. Allegiance requires a cause; a cause requires an enemy. This much is obvious; the critical point is that the enemy that defines the cause must seem genuinely formidable. Roughly speaking, the presumed power of the "enemy" sufficient to warrant an individual sense of allegiance to a society must be proportionate to the size and complexity of the society. Today, of course, that power must be one of unprecedented magnitude and frightfulness.

It follows, from the patterns of human behavior, that

the credibility of a social "enemy" demands similarly a readiness of response in proportion to its menace. In a broad social context, "an eye for an eye" still characterizes the only acceptable attitude toward a presumed threat of aggression, despite contrary religious and moral precepts governing personal conduct. The remoteness of personal decision from social consequence in a modern society makes it easy for its members to maintain this attitude without being aware of it. A recent example is the war in Vietnam; a less recent one was the bombing of Hiroshima and Nagasaki.[9] In each case, the extent and gratuitousness of the slaughter were abstracted into political formulae by most Americans, once the proposition that the victims were "enemies" was established. The war system makes such an abstracted response possible in nonmilitary contexts as well. A conventional example of this mechanism is the inability of most people to connect, let us say, the starvation of millions in India with their own past conscious political decision-making. Yet the sequential logic linking a decision to restrict grain production in America with an eventual famine in Asia is obvious, unambiguous, and unconcealed.

What gives the war system its preeminent role in social organization, as elsewhere, is its unmatched authority over life and death. It must be emphasized again that the war system is not a mere social extension of the presumed need for individual human violence, but itself in turn serves to rationalize most nonmilitary killing. It also provides the precedent for the collective willingness of members of a society to pay a blood price for institutions far less central to social organization than war. To take a handy example, ". . . rather than accept speed limits of twenty miles an hour we prefer to let automobiles kill forty thousand people a year."[10] A Rand analyst puts it in more general terms and less rhetorically: "I am sure that there is, in effect, a desirable level of automobile accidents—desirable, that is, from a broad point of view; in the sense that it is a necessary concomitant of things of greater value to society."[11] The point may seem too obvious for iteration, but it is essential to an understanding of the important motivational function of war as a model for collective sacrifice.

A brief look at some defunct premodern societies is instructive. One of the most noteworthy features common to the larger, more complex, and more successful of ancient civilizations was their widespread use of the blood sacrifice. If one were to limit consideration to those cultures whose regional hegemony was so complete that the prospect of "war" had become virtually inconceivable —as was the case with several of the great pre-Columbian societies of the Western Hemisphere—it would be found that some form of ritual killing occupied a position of paramount social importance in each. Invariably, the ritual was invested with mythic or religious significance; as with all religious and totemic practice, however, the ritual masked a broader and more important social function.

In these societies, the blood sacrifice served the purpose of maintaining a vestigial "earnest" of the society's capability and willingness to make war—i.e., kill and be killed—in the event that some mystical—i.e., unforeseen —circumstance were to give rise to the possibility. That the "earnest" was not an adequate substitute for genuine military organization when the unthinkable enemy, such as the Spanish conquistadores, actually appeared on the scene in no way negates the function of the ritual. It was primarily, if not exclusively, a symbolic reminder that war had once been the central organizing force of the society, and that this condition might recur.

It does not follow that a transition to total peace in modern societies would require the use of this model, even in less "barbaric" guise. But the historical analogy serves as a reminder that a viable substitute for war as a social system cannot be a mere symbolic charade. It must involve real risk of real personal destruction, and on a scale consistent with the size and complexity of modern social systems. Credibility is the key. Whether the substitute is ritual in nature or functionally substantive, unless it provides a believable life-and-death threat it will not serve the socially organizing function of war.

The existence of an accepted external menace, then, is essential to social cohesiveness as well as to the acceptance of political authority. The menace must be believable, it must be of a magnitude consistent with the complexity of the society threatened, and it must appear, at least, to affect the entire society.

Ecological

Man, like all other animals, is subject to the continuing process of adapting to the limitations of his environment. But the principal mechanism he has utilized for this purpose is unique among living creatures. To forestall the inevitable historical cycles of inadequate food supply, post-Neolithic man destroys surplus members of his own species by organized warfare.

Ethologists[12] have often observed that the organized slaughter of members of their own species is virtually unknown among other animals. Man's special propensity to kill his own kind (shared to a limited degree with rats) may be attributed to his inability to adapt anachronistic patterns of survival (like primitive hunting) to his development of "civilizations" in which these patterns cannot be effectively sublimated. It may be attributed to other causes that have been suggested, such as a maladapted "territorial instinct," etc. Nevertheless, it exists and its social expression in war constitutes a biological control of his relationship to his natural environment that is peculiar to man alone.

War has served to help assure the *survival* of the human species. But as an evolutionary device to *improve* it, war is almost unbelievably inefficient. With few exceptions, the selective processes of other living creatures promote both specific survival *and* genetic improvement. When a conventionally adaptive animal faces one of its periodic crises of insufficiency, it is the "inferior" members of the species that normally disappear. An animal's social response to such a crisis may take the form of a mass migration, during which the weak fall by the wayside. Or it may follow the dramatic and more efficient pattern of lemming societies, in which the weaker members voluntarily disperse, leaving available food supplies for the stronger. In either case, the strong survive and the weak fall. In human societies, those who fight and die in wars for survival are in general its biologically stronger members. This is natural selection in reverse.

The regressive genetic effect of war has been often noted[13] and equally often deplored, even when it confuses biological and cultural factors.[14] The disproportionate loss of the *biologically* stronger remains inherent in traditional warfare. It serves to underscore the fact that survival of the species, rather than its improvement, is the fundamental purpose of natural selection, if it can be said to have a purpose, just as it is the basic premise of this study.

But as the polemologist Gaston Bouthoul[15] has pointed out, other institutions that were developed to serve this ecological function have proved even less satisfactory. (They include such established forms as these: infanticide, practiced chiefly in ancient and primitive societies; sexual mutilation; monasticism; forced emigration; extensive capital punishment, as in old China and eighteenth-century England; and other similar, usually localized, practices.)

Man's ability to increase his productivity of the essentials of physical life suggests that the need for protection against cyclical famine may be nearly obsolete.[16] It has thus tended to reduce the apparent importance of the basic ecological function of war, which is generally disregarded by peace theorists. Two aspects of it remain especially relevant, however. The first is obvious: current rates of population growth, compounded by environmental threat of chemical and other contaminants, may well bring about a new crisis of insufficiency. If so, it is likely to be one of unprecedented global magnitude, not merely regional or temporary. Conventional methods of warfare would almost surely prove inadequate, in this event, to reduce the consuming population to a level consistent with survival of the species.

The second relevant factor is the efficiency of modern methods of mass destruction. Even if their use is not required to meet a world population crisis, they offer, perhaps paradoxically, the first opportunity in the history of man to halt the regressive genetic effects of natural selection by war. Nuclear weapons are indiscriminate. Their application would bring to an end the disproportionate destruction of the physically stronger members of the species (the "warriors") in periods of war. Whether this prospect of genetic gain would offset the unfavorable mutations anticipated from postnuclear radioactivity we have not yet determined. What gives the question a bearing on our study is the possibility that the determination may yet have to be made.

Another secondary ecological trend bearing on projected population growth is the regressive effect of certain medical advances. Pestilence, for example, is no longer an important factor in population control. The problem of increased life expectancy has been aggravated. These advances also pose a potentially more sinister problem, in that undesirable genetic traits that were formerly self-liquidating are now medically maintained.

Many diseases that were once fatal at preprocreational ages are now cured; the effect of this development is to perpetuate undesirable susceptibilities and mutations. It seems clear that a new quasi-eugenic function of war is now in process of formation that will have to be taken into account in any transition plan. For the time being, the Department of Defense appears to have recognized such factors, as has been demonstrated by the planning under way by the Rand Corporation to cope with the breakdown in the ecological balance anticipated after a thermonuclear war. The Department has also begun to stockpile birds, for example, against the expected pro- liferation of radiation-resistant insects, etc.

Cultural and Scientific

The declared order of values in modern societies gives a high place to the so-called "creative" activities, and an even higher one to those associated with the advance of scientific knowledge. Widely held social values can be translated into political equivalents, which in turn may bear on the nature of a transition to peace. The attitudes of those who hold these values must be taken into ac- count in the planning of the transition. The dependence, therefore, of cultural and scientific achievement on the war system would be an important consideration in a transition plan even if such achievement had no inher- ently necessary social function.

Of all the countless dichotomies invented by scholars to account for the major differences in art styles and cycles, only one has been consistently unambiguous in its application to a variety of forms and cultures. However it may be verbalized, the basic distinction is this: Is the work war-oriented or is it not? Among primitive peoples, the war dance is the most important art form. Elsewhere, literature, music, painting, sculpture, and architecture that has won lasting acceptance has invariably dealt with a theme of war, expressly or implicitly, and has expressed the centricity of war to society. The war in question may be national conflict, as in Shakespeare plays, Beethoven's music, or Goya's paintings, or it may be reflected in the form of religious, social, or moral struggle, as in the work of Dante, Rembrandt, and Bach. Art that cannot be classified as war-oriented is usually described as "sterile," "decadent," and so on. Application of the "war standard" to works of art may often leave room for debate in individual cases, but there is no question of its role as the fundamental determinant of cultural values. Aesthetic and moral standards have a common anthropological origin, in the exaltation of bravery, the willingness to kill and risk death in tribal warfare.

It is also instructive to note that the character of a society's culture has borne a close relationship to its war-making potential, in the context of its times. It is no accident that the current "cultural explosion" in the United States is taking place during an era marked by an unusually rapid advance in weaponry. This relationship is more generally recognized than the literature on the subject would suggest. For example, many artists and writers are now beginning to express concern over the limited creative options they envisage in the warless world they think, or hope, may be soon upon us. They are currently preparing for this possibility by unprecedented experimentation with meaningless forms; their interest in recent years has been increasingly engaged by the abstract pattern, the gratuitous emotion, the random happening, and the unrelated sequence.

The relationship of war to scientific research and discovery is more explicit. War is the principal motivational force for the development of science at every level, from the abstractly conceptual to the narrowly technological. Modern society places a high value on "pure" science, but it is historically inescapable that all the significant discoveries that have been made about the natural world have been inspired by the real or imaginary military necessities of their epochs. The consequences of the discoveries have indeed gone far afield, but war has always provided the basic incentive.

Beginning with the development of iron and steel, and proceeding through the discoveries of the laws of motion and thermodynamics to the age of the atomic particle, the synthetic polymer, and the space capsule, no important scientific advance has not been at least indirectly initiated by an implicit requirement of weaponry. More prosaic examples include the transistor radio (an outgrowth of military communications requirements), the assembly line (from Civil War firearms needs), the steel-frame building (from the steel battleship), the canal lock, and so on. A typical adaptation can be seen in a device as modest as the common lawnmower; it developed from the revolving scythe devised by Leonardo da Vinci to precede a horse-powered vehicle into enemy ranks.

The most direct relationship can be found in medical technology. For example, a giant "walking machine," an amplifier of body motions invented for military use in difficult terrain, is now making it possible for many previously confined to wheelchairs to walk. The Vietnam war alone has led to spectacular improvements in amputation procedures, blood-handling techniques, and surgical logistics. It has stimulated new large-scale research on malaria and other tropical parasite diseases; it is hard to estimate how long this work would otherwise have been delayed, despite its enormous nonmilitary importance to nearly half the world's population.

Other

We have elected to omit from our discussion of the nonmilitary functions of war those we do not consider critical to a transition program. This is not to say they are unimportant, however, but only that they appear to present no special problems for the organization of a peace-oriented social system. They include the following:

War as a general social release. This is a psychosocial function, serving the same purpose for a society as do the holiday, the celebration, and the orgy for the individual—the release and redistribution of undifferentiated tensions. War provides for the periodic necessary readjustment of standards of social behavior (the "moral climate") and for the dissipation of general boredom, one of the most consistently undervalued and unrecognized of social phenomena.

War as a generational stabilizer. This psychological

function, served by other behavior patterns in other animals, enables the physically deteriorating older generation to maintain its control of the younger, destroying it if necessary.

War as an ideological clarifier. The dualism that characterizes the traditional dialectic of all branches of philosophy and of stable political relationships stems from war as the prototype of conflict. Except for secondary considerations, there cannot be, to put it as simply as possible, more than two sides to a question because there cannot be more than two sides to a war.

War as the basis for inter-national understanding. Before the development of modern communications, the strategic requirements of war provided the only substantial incentive for the enrichment of one national culture with the achievements of another. Although this is still the case in many inter-national relationships, the function is obsolescent.

We have also forgone extended characterization of those functions we assume to be widely and explicitly recognized. An obvious example is the role of war as controller of the quality and degree of unemployment. This is more than an economic and political subfunction; its sociological, cultural, and ecological aspects are also important, although often teleonomic. But none affect the general problem of substitution. The same is true of certain other functions; those we have included are sufficient to define the scope of the problem.

SUBSTITUTES FOR THE FUNCTIONS OF WAR

By now it should be clear that the most detailed and comprehensive master plan for a transition to world peace will remain academic if it fails to deal forthrightly with the problem of the critical nonmilitary functions of war. The social needs they serve are essential; if the war system no longer exists to meet them, substitute institutions will have to be established for the purpose. These surrogates must be "realistic," which is to say of a scope and nature that can be conceived and implemented in the context of present-day social capabilities. This is not the truism it may appear to be; the requirements of radical social change often reveal the distinction between a most conservative projection and a wildly utopian scheme to be fine indeed.

In this section we will consider some possible substitutes for these functions. Only in rare instances have they been put forth for the purposes which concern us here, but we see no reason to limit ourselves to proposals that address themselves explicitly to the problem as we have outlined it. We will disregard the ostensible, or military, functions of war; it is a premise of this study that the transition to peace implies absolutely that they will no longer exist in any relevant sense. We will also disregard the noncritical functions exemplified at the end of the preceding section.

Economic

Economic surrogates for war must meet two principal criteria. They must be "wasteful," in the common sense of the word, and they must operate outside the normal supply-demand system. A corollary that should be obvious is that the magnitude of the waste must be sufficient to meet the needs of a particular society. An economy as advanced and complex as our own requires the planned average annual destruction of not less than 10 percent of gross national product[1] if it is effectively to fulfill its stabilizing function. When the mass of a balance wheel is inadequate to the power it is intended to control, its effect can be self-defeating, as with a runaway locomotive. The analogy, though crude,[2] is especially apt for the American economy, as our record of cyclical depressions shows. All have taken place during periods of grossly inadequate military spending.

Those few economic conversion programs which by

implication acknowledge the nonmilitary economic function of war (at least to some extent) tend to assume that so-called social-welfare expenditures will fill the vacuum created by the disappearance of military spending. When one considers the backlog of unfinished business—proposed but still unexecuted—in this field, the assumption seems plausible. Let us examine briefly the following list, which is more or less typical of general social welfare programs.[3]

Health. Drastic expansion of medical research, education, and training facilities; hospital and clinic construction; the general objective of *complete* government-guaranteed health care for all, at a level consistent with current developments in medical technology.

Education. The equivalent of the foregoing in teacher training; schools and libraries; the drastic upgrading of standards, with the general objective of making available for all an attainable educational goal equivalent to what is now considered a professional degree.

Housing. Clean, comfortable, safe, and spacious living space for all, at the level now enjoyed by about 15 percent of the population in this country (less in most others).

Transportation. The establishment of a system of mass public transportation making it possible for all to travel to and from areas of work and recreation quickly, comfortably, and conveniently, and to travel privately for pleasure rather than necessity.

Physical environment. The development and protec-

tion of water supplies, forests, parks, and other natural
resources; the elimination of chemical and bacterial contaminants from air, water, and soil.

Poverty. The genuine elimination of poverty, defined by a standard consistent with current economic productivity, by means of a guaranteed annual income or
whatever system of distribution will best assure its
achievement.

This is only a sampler of the more obvious domestic
social welfare items, and we have listed it in a deliberately broad, perhaps extravagant, manner. In the past,
such a vague and ambitious-sounding "program" would
have been dismissed out of hand, without serious consideration; it would clearly have been, *prima facie*, far
too costly, quite apart from its political implications.[4]
Our objection to it, on the other hand, could hardly be
more contradictory. As an economic substitute for war,
it is inadequate because it would be far too cheap.

If this seems paradoxical, it must be remembered
that up to now all proposed social-welfare expenditures
have had to be measured *within* the war economy, not as
a replacement for it. The old slogan about a battleship
or an ICBM costing as much as x hospitals or y schools
or z homes takes on a very different meaning if there are
to be no more battleships or ICBM's.

Since the list is general, we have elected to forestall
the tangential controversy that surrounds arbitrary cost
projections by offering no individual cost estimates. But
the maximum program that could be physically effected
along the lines indicated could approach the established

level of military spending only for a limited time—in our opinion, subject to a detailed cost-and-feasibility analysis, less than ten years. In this short period, at this rate, the major goals of the program would have been achieved. Its capital-investment phase would have been completed, and it would have established a permanent comparatively modest level of annual operating cost— *within the framework of the general economy.*

Here is the basic weakness of the social-welfare surrogate. On the short-term basis, a maximum program of this sort could replace a normal military spending program, provided it was designed, like the military model, to be subject to arbitrary control. Public housing starts, for example, or the development of modern medical centers might be accelerated or halted from time to time, as the requirements of a stable economy might dictate. But on the long-term basis, social-welfare spending, no matter how often redefined, would necessarily become an integral, accepted part of the economy, of no more value as a stabilizer than the automobile industry or old age and survivors' insurance. Apart from whatever merit social-welfare programs are deemed to have for their own sake, their function as a substitute for war in the economy would thus be self-liquidating. They might serve, however, as expedients pending the development of more durable substitute measures.

Another economic surrogate that has been proposed is a series of giant "space research" programs. These have already demonstrated their utility in more modest scale within the military economy. What has been implied, although not yet expressly put forth, is the development of a long-range sequence of space-research projects with largely unattainable goals. This kind of program offers several advantages lacking in the social welfare model. First, it is unlikely to phase itself out, regardless of the predictable "surprises" science has in store for us: the universe is too big. In the event some individual project unexpectedly succeeds there would be no dearth of substitute problems. For example, if colonization of the moon proceeds on schedule, it could then become "necessary" to establish a beachhead on Mars or Jupiter, and so on. Second, it need be no more dependent on the general supply-demand economy than its military prototype. Third, it lends itself extraordinarily well to arbitrary control.

Space research can be viewed as the nearest modern equivalent yet devised to the pyramid-building, and similar ritualistic enterprises, of ancient societies. It is true that the scientific value of the space program, even of what has already been accomplished, is substantial on its own terms. But current programs are absurdly and obviously disproportionate, in the relationship of the knowledge sought to the expenditures committed. All but a small fraction of the space budget, measured by the standards of comparable scientific objectives, must be charged *de facto* to the military economy. Future space research, projected as a war surrogate, would further reduce the "scientific" rationale of its budget to a minuscule percentage indeed. As a purely economic substitute for war, therefore, extension of the space program warrants serious consideration.

In Section 3 we pointed out that certain disarmament models, which we called conservative, postulated extremely expensive and elaborate inspection systems. Would it be possible to extend and institutionalize such systems to the point where they might serve as economic surrogates for war spending? The organization of fail-safe inspection machinery could well be ritualized in a manner similar to that of established military processes. "Inspection teams" might be very like armies, and their technical equipment might be very like weapons. Inflating the inspection budget to military scale presents no difficulty. The appeal of this kind of scheme lies in the comparative ease of transition between two parallel systems.

The "elaborate inspection" surrogate is fundamentally fallacious, however. Although it might be economically useful, as well as politically necessary, during the disarmament transition, it would fail as a substitute for the economic function of war for one simple reason. Peace-keeping inspection is part of a war system, not of a peace system. It implies the possibility of weapons maintenance or manufacture, which could not exist in a world at peace as here defined. Massive inspection also implies sanctions, and thus war-readiness.

The same fallacy is more obvious in plans to create a patently useless "defense conversion" apparatus. The long-discredited proposal to build "total" civil defense facilities is one example; another is the plan to establish a giant antimissile missile complex (Nike-X, *et al.*). These programs, of course, are economic rather than strategic. Nevertheless, they are not substitutes for military spending but merely different forms of it.

A more sophisticated variant is the proposal to establish the "Unarmed Forces" of the United States.[5] This would conveniently maintain the entire institutional military structure, redirecting it essentially toward social-welfare activities on a global scale. It would be, in effect, a giant military Peace Corps. There is nothing inherently unworkable about this plan, and using the existing military system to effectuate its own demise is both ingenious and convenient. But even on a greatly magnified world basis, social-welfare expenditures must sooner or later reenter the atmosphere of the normal economy. The practical transitional virtues of such a scheme would thus be eventually negated by its inadequacy as a permanent economic stabilizer.

Political

The war system makes the stable government of societies possible. It does this essentially by providing an external necessity for a society to accept political rule. In so doing, it establishes the basis for nationhood and the authority of government to control its constituents. What other institution or combination of programs might serve these functions in its place?

We have already pointed out that the end of war means the end of national sovereignty, and thus the end of nationhood as we know it today. But this does not necessarily mean the end of nations in the administrative sense, and internal political power will remain essential to a stable society. The emerging "nations" of the peace epoch must continue to draw political authority from some source.

A number of proposals have been made governing the relations between nations after total disarmament; all are basically juridical in nature. They contemplate institutions more or less like a World Court, or a United Nations, but vested with real authority. They may or may not serve their ostensible postmilitary purpose of settling international disputes, but we need not discuss that here. None would offer effective external pressure on a peace-world nation to organize itself politically.

It might be argued that a well-armed international police force, operating under the authority of such a supranational "court," could well serve the function of external enemy. This, however, would constitute a military operation, like the inspection schemes mentioned, and, like them, would be inconsistent with the premise of an end to the war system. It is possible that a variant of the "Unarmed Forces" idea might be developed in such a way that its "constructive" (i.e., social welfare) activities could be combined with an economic "threat" of sufficient size and credibility to warrant political organization. Would this kind of threat also be contradictory to our basic premise?—that is, would it be inevitably military? Not necessarily, in our view, but we are skeptical of its capacity to evoke credibility. Also, the obvious destabilizing effect of any global social welfare surrogate on politically necessary class relationships would create an entirely new set of transition problems at least equal in magnitude.

Credibility, in fact, lies at the heart of the problem of developing a political substitute for war. This is where the space-race proposals, in many ways so well suited as economic substitutes for war, fall short. The most ambitious and unrealistic space project cannot of itself generate a believable external menace. It has been hotly argued[6] that such a menace would offer the "last, best hope of peace," etc., by uniting mankind against the danger of destruction by "creatures" from other planets or from outer space. Experiments have been proposed to test the credibility of an out-of-our-world invasion threat; it is possible that a few of the more difficult-to-explain "flying saucer" incidents of recent years were in fact early experiments of this kind. If so, they could hardly have been judged encouraging. We anticipate no difficulties in making a "need" for a giant super space program credible for economic purposes, even were there not ample precedent; extending it, for political purposes, to include features unfortunately associated with science fiction would obviously be a more dubious undertaking.

Nevertheless, an effective political substitute for war would require "alternate enemies," some of which might seem equally farfetched in the context of the current war system. It may be, for instance, that gross pollution of the environment can eventually replace the possibility of mass destruction by nuclear weapons as the principal apparent threat to the survival of the species. Poisoning of the air, and of the principal sources of food and water supply, is already well advanced, and at first glance would seem promising in this respect; it constitutes a threat that can be dealt with only through social organization and political power. But from present indications it will be a generation to a generation and a half before environmental pollution, however severe, will be sufficiently menacing, on a global scale, to offer a possible basis for a solution.

It is true that the rate of pollution could be increased selectively for this purpose; in fact, the mere modifying of existing programs for the deterrence of pollution could speed up the process enough to make the threat credible much sooner. But the pollution problem has been so widely publicized in recent years that it seems highly improbable that a program of deliberate environmental poisoning could be implemented in a politically acceptable manner.

However unlikely some of the possible alternate enemies we have mentioned may seem, we must emphasize that one *must* be found, of credible quality and magnitude, if a transition to peace is ever to come about without social disintegration. It is more probable, in our judgment, that such a threat will have to be invented, rather than developed from unknown conditions. For this reason, we believe further speculation about its putative nature ill-advised in this context. Since there is considerable doubt, in our minds, that *any* viable political surrogate can be devised, we are reluctant to compromise, by premature discussion, any possible option that may eventually lie open to our government.

Sociological

Of the many functions of war we have found convenient to group together in this classification, two are critical. In a world of peace, the continuing stability of society will require: 1) an effective substitute for military institutions that can neutralize destabilizing social elements and 2) a credible motivational surrogate for war that can insure social cohesiveness. The first is an essential element of social control; the second is the basic mechanism for adapting individual human drives to the needs of society.

Most proposals that address themselves, explicitly or otherwise, to the postwar problem of controlling the socially alienated turn to some variant of the Peace Corps or the so-called Job Corps for a solution. The socially disaffected, the economically unprepared, the psychologically unconformable, the hard-core "delinquents," the incorrigible "subversives," and the rest of the unemployable are seen as somehow transformed by the disciplines of a service modeled on military precedent into more or less dedicated social service workers. This presumption also informs the otherwise hardheaded ratiocination of the "Unarmed Forces" plan.

The problem has been addressed, in the language of popular sociology, by Secretary McNamara. "Even in our abundant societies, we have reason enough to worry over the tensions that coil and tighten among under-privileged young people, and finally flail out in delin-quency and crime. What are we to expect . . . where mounting frustrations are likely to fester into eruptions of violence and extremism?" In a seemingly unrelated passage, he continues: "It seems to me that we could move toward remedying that inequity [of the Selective Service System] by asking every young person in the United States to give two years of service to his country —whether in one of the military services, in the Peace Corps, or in some other volunteer developmental work at home or abroad. We could encourage other countries to do the same."[7] Here, as elsewhere throughout this significant speech, Mr. McNamara has focused, indirectly but unmistakably, on one of the key issues bearing on a possible transition to peace, and has later indicated, also indirectly, a rough approach to its resolution, again phrased in the language of the current war system.

It seems clear that Mr. McNamara and other propo-nents of the peace-corps surrogate for this war function lean heavily on the success of the paramilitary Depres-sion programs mentioned in the last section. We find the precedent wholly inadequate in degree. Neither the lack of relevant precedent, however, nor the dubious social-welfare sentimentality characterizing this approach war-rant its rejection without careful study. It may be viable —provided, first, that the military origin of the Corps for-mat be effectively rendered out of its operational activity, and second, that the transition from paramilitary activities to "developmental work" can be effected without regard to the attitudes of the Corps personnel or to the "value" of the work it is expected to perform.

Another possible surrogate for the control of potential enemies of society is the reintroduction, in some form consistent with modern technology and political processes, of slavery. Up to now, this has been suggested only in fiction, notably in the works of Wells, Huxley, Orwell, and others engaged in the imaginative anticipation of the sociology of the future. But the fantasies projected in *Brave New World* and *1984* have seemed less and less implausible over the years since their publication. The traditional association of slavery with ancient preindustrial cultures should not blind us to its adaptability to advanced forms of social organization, nor should its equally traditional incompatibility with Western moral and economic values. It is entirely possible that the development of a sophisticated form of slavery may be an absolute prerequisite for social control in a world at peace. As a practical matter, conversion of the code of military discipline to a euphemized form of enslavement would entail surprisingly little revision; the logical first step would be the adoption of some form of "universal" military service.

When it comes to postulating a credible substitute for war capable of directing human behavior patterns in behalf of social organization, few options suggest themselves. Like its political function, the motivational function of war requires the existence of a genuinely menacing social enemy. The principal difference is that for purposes of motivating basic allegiance, as distinct from accepting political authority, the "alternate enemy" must imply a more immediate, tangible, and directly felt threat of destruction. It must justify the need for taking and paying a "blood price" in wide areas of human concern.

In this respect, the possible substitute enemies noted earlier would be insufficient. One exception might be the environmental-pollution model, if the danger to society it posed was genuinely imminent. The fictive models would have to carry the weight of extraordinary conviction, underscored with a not inconsiderable actual sacrifice of life; the construction of an up-to-date mythological or religious structure for this purpose would present difficulties in our era, but must certainly be considered.

Games theorists have suggested, in other contexts, the development of "blood games" for the effective control of individual aggressive impulses. It is an ironic commentary on the current state of war and peace studies that it was left not to scientists but to the makers of a commercial film[8] to develop a model for this notion, on the implausible level of popular melodrama, as a ritualized manhunt. More realistically, such a ritual might be socialized, in the manner of the Spanish Inquisition and the less formal witch trials of other periods, for purposes of "social purification," "state security," or other rationale both acceptable and credible to postwar societies. The feasibility of such an updated version of still another ancient institution, though doubtful, is considerably less fanciful than the wishful notion of many peace planners that a lasting condition of peace can be brought about without the most painstaking examination of every possible surrogate for the essential functions of war. What is involved here, in a sense, is the quest for William James's "moral equivalent of war."

It is also possible that the two functions considered under this heading may be jointly served, in the sense of establishing the antisocial, for whom a control institution is needed, as the "alternate enemy" needed to hold society together. The relentless and irreversible advance of unemployability at all levels of society, and the similar extension of generalized alienation from accepted values[9] may make some such program necessary even as an adjunct to the war system. As before, we will not speculate on the specific forms this kind of program might take, except to note that there is again ample precedent, in the treament meted out to disfavored, allegedly menacing, ethnic groups in certain societies during certain historical periods.[10]

Ecological

Considering the shortcomings of war as a mechanism of selective population control, it might appear that devising substitutes for this function should be comparatively simple. Schematically this is so, but the problem of timing the transition to a new ecological balancing device makes the feasibility of substitution less certain.

It must be remembered that the limitation of war in this function is entirely eugenic. War has not been genetically progressive. But as a system of gross population control to preserve the species it cannot fairly be faulted. And, as has been pointed out, the nature of war is itself in transition. Current trends in warfare—the increased strategic bombing of civilians and the greater military importance now attached to the destruction of sources of supply (as opposed to purely "military" bases and personnel)—strongly suggest that a truly qualitative improvement is in the making. Assuming the war system is to continue, it is more than probable that the regressively selective quality of war will have been reversed, as its victims become more genetically representative of their societies.

There is no question but that a universal requirement that procreation be limited to the products of artificial insemination would provide a fully adequate substitute control for population levels. Such a reproductive system would, of course, have the added advantage of being susceptible of direct eugenic management. Its predictable further development—conception and embryonic growth taking place wholly under laboratory conditions —would extend these controls to their logical conclusion. The ecological function of war under these circumstances would not only be superseded but surpassed in effectiveness.

The indicated intermediate step—total control of conception with a variant of the ubiquitous "pill," via water supplies or certain essential foodstuffs, offset by a controlled "antidote"—is already under development.[11] There would appear to be no foreseeable need to revert to any of the outmoded practices referred to in the previous section (infanticide, etc.) as there might have been if the possibility of transition to peace had arisen two generations ago.

The real question here, therefore, does not concern the viability of this war substitute, but the political problems involved in bringing it about. It cannot be established while the war system is still in effect. The reason for this is simple: excess population is war material. As long as any society must contemplate even a remote possibility of war, it must maintain a maximum supportable population, even when so doing critically aggravates an economic liability. This is paradoxical, in view of war's role in reducing excess population, but it is readily understood. War controls the *general* population level, but the ecological interest of any single society lies in maintaining its hegemony vis-à-vis other societies. The obvious analogy can be seen in any free-enterprise economy. Practices damaging to the society as a whole—both competitive and monopolistic—are abetted by the conflicting economic motives of individual capital interests. The obvious precedent can be found in the seemingly irrational political difficulties which have blocked universal adoption of simple birth-control methods. Nations desperately in need of increasing unfavorable production-consumption ratios are nevertheless unwilling to gamble their possible military requirements of twenty years hence for this purpose. Unilateral population control, as practiced in ancient Japan and in other isolated societies, is out of the question in today's world.

Since the eugenic solution cannot be achieved until the transition to the peace system takes place, why not wait? One must qualify the inclination to agree. As we noted earlier, a real possibility of an unprecedented global crisis of insufficiency exists today, which the war system may not be able to forestall. If this should come to pass before an agreed-upon transition to peace were completed, the result might be irrevocably disastrous. There is clearly no solution to this dilemma; it is a risk which must be taken. But it tends to support the view that if a decision is made to elminate the war system, it were better done sooner than later.

Cultural and Scientific

Strictly speaking, the function of war as the determinant of cultural values and as the prime mover of scientific progress may not be critical in a world without war. Our criterion for the basic nonmilitary functions of war has been: Are they necessary to the survival and stability of society? The absolute need for substitute cultural value-determinants and for the continued advance of scientific knowledge is not established. We believe it important, however, in behalf of those for whom these functions hold subjective significance, that it be known what they can reasonably expect in culture and science after a transition to peace.

So far as the creative arts are concerned, there is no reason to believe they would disappear, but only that they would change in character and relative social importance. The elimination of war would in due course

deprive them of their principal conative force, but it
would necessarily take some time for the effect of this
withdrawal to be felt. During the transition, and perhaps
for a generation thereafter, themes of sociomoral conflict
inspired by the war system would be increasingly trans-
ferred to the idiom of purely personal sensibility. At the
same time, a new aesthetic would have to develop. Whatever its name, form, or rationale, its function would be
to express, in language appropriate to the new period,
the once discredited philosophy that art exists for its own
sake. This aesthetic would reject unequivocally the clas-
sic requirement of paramilitary conflict as the substantive content of great art. The eventual effect of the
peace-world philosophy of art would be democratizing
in the extreme, in the sense that a generally acknowledged subjectivity of artistic standards would equalize
their new, content-free "values."

What may be expected to happen is that art would
be reassigned the role it once played in a few primitive
peace-oriented social systems. This was the function of
pure decoration, entertainment, or play, entirely free
of the burden of expressing the sociomoral values and
conflicts of a war-oriented society. It is interesting that
the groundwork for such a value-free aesthetic is already
being laid today, in growing experimentation in art without content, perhaps in anticipation of a world without
conflict. A cult has developed around a new kind of
cultural determinism,[12] which proposes that the technological form of a cultural expression determines its values
rather than does its ostensibly meaningful content. Its

clear implication is that there is no "good" or "bad" art, only that which is appropriate to its (technological) times and that which is not. Its cultural effect has been to promote circumstantial constructions and unplanned expressions; it denies to art the relevance of sequential logic. Its significance in this context is that it provides a working model of one kind of value-free culture we might reasonably anticipate in a world at peace.

So far as science is concerned, it might appear at first glance that a giant space-research program, the most promising among the proposed economic surrogates for war, might also serve as the basic stimulator of scientific research. The lack of fundamental organized social conflict inherent in space work, however, would rule it out as an adequate motivational substitute for war when applied to "pure" science. But it could no doubt sustain the broad range of *technological* activity that a space budget of military dimensions would require. A similarly scaled social-welfare program could provide a comparable impetus to low-keyed technological advances, especially in medicine, rationalized construction methods, educational psychology, etc. The eugenic substitute for the ecological function of war would also require continuing research in certain areas of the life sciences.

Apart from these partial substitutes for war, it must be kept in mind that the momentum given to scientific progress by the great wars of the past century, and even more by the anticipation of World War III, is intellectually and materially enormous. It is our finding that if the war system were to end tomorrow this momentum is so great that the pursuit of scientific knowledge could reasonably be expected to go forward without noticeable diminution for perhaps two decades.[13] It would then continue, at a progressively decreasing tempo, for at least another two decades before the "bank account" of today's unresolved problems would become exhausted. By the standards of the questions we have learned to ask today, there would no longer be anything worth knowing still unknown; we cannot conceive, by definition, of the scientific questions to ask once those we can now comprehend are answered.

This leads unavoidably to another matter: the intrinsic value of the unlimited search for knowledge. We of course offer no independent value judgments here, but it is germane to point out that a substantial minority of scientific opinion feels that search to be circumscribed in any case. This opinion is itself a factor in considering the need for a substitute for the scientific function of war. For the record, we must also take note of the precedent that during long periods of human history, often covering thousands of years, in which no intrinsic social value was assigned to scientific progress, stable societies did survive and flourish. Although this could not have been possible in the modern industrial world, we cannot be certain it may not again be true in a future world at peace.

SECTION 7

SUMMARY AND CONCLUSIONS

The Nature of War

WAR IS NOT, as is widely assumed, primarily an instrument of policy utilized by nations to extend or defend their expressed political values or their economic interests. On the contrary, it is itself the principal basis of organization on which all modern societies are constructed. The common proximate cause of war is the apparent interference of one nation with the aspirations of another. But at the root of all ostensible differences of national interest lie the dynamic requirements of the war system itself for periodic armed conflict. Readiness for war characterizes contemporary social systems more broadly than their economic and political structures, which it subsumes.

79

Economic analyses of the anticipated problems of transition to peace have not recognized the broad preeminence of war in the definition of social systems. The same is true, with rare and only partial exceptions, of model disarmament "scenarios." For this reason, the value of this previous work is limited to the mechanical aspects of transition. Certain features of these models may perhaps be applicable to a real situation of conversion to peace; this will depend on their compatibility with a substantive, rather than a procedural, peace plan. Such a plan can be developed only from the premise of full understanding of the nature of the war system it proposes to abolish, which in turn presupposes detailed comprehension of the functions the war system performs for society. It will require the construction of a detailed and feasible system of substitutes for those functions that are necessary to the stability and survival of human societies.

The Functions of War

The visible, military function of war requires no elucidation; it is not only obvious but also irrelevant to a transition to the condition of peace, in which it will by definition be superfluous. It is also subsidiary in social significance to the implied, nonmilitary functions of war; those critical to transition can be summarized in five principal groupings.

1. Economic. War has provided both ancient and modern societies with a dependable system for stabilizing and controlling national economies. No alternate method of control has yet been tested in a complex modern economy that has shown itself remotely comparable in scope or effectiveness.

2. *Political.* The permanent possibility of war is the foundation for stable government; it supplies the basis for general acceptance of political authority. It has enabled societies to maintain necessary class distinctions, and it has ensured the subordination of the citizen to the state, by virtue of the residual war powers inherent in the concept of nationhood. No modern political ruling group has successfully controlled its constituency after failing to sustain the continuing credibility of an external threat of war.

3. *Sociological.* War, through the medium of military institutions, has uniquely served societies, throughout the course of known history, as an indispensable controller of dangerous social dissidence and destructive antisocial tendencies. As the most formidable of threats to life itself, and as the only one susceptible to mitigation by social organization alone, it has played another equally fundamental role: the war system has provided the machinery through which the motivational forces governing human behavior have been translated into binding social allegiance. It has thus ensured the degree of social cohesion necessary to the viability of nations. No other institution, or groups of institutions, in modern societies, has successfully served these functions.

4. *Ecological.* War has been the principal evolutionary device for maintaining a satisfactory ecological balance between gross human population and supplies

available for its survival. It is unique to the human
species.

5. *Cultural and Scientific.*   War-orientation has determined the basic standards of value in the creative arts,
and has provided the fundamental motivational source of
scientific and technological progress. The concepts that
the arts express values independent of their own forms
and that the successful pursuit of knowledge has intrinsic
social value have long been accepted in modern societies;
the development of the arts and sciences during this
period has been corollary to the parallel development of
weaponry.

Substitutes for the Functions of War: Criteria

The foregoing functions of war are essential to the
survival of the social systems we know today. With two
possible exceptions they are also essential to any kind
of stable social organization that might survive in a warless world. Discussion of the ways and means of transition to such a world are meaningless unless a) substitute
institutions can be devised to fill these functions, or b) it
can reasonably be hypothecated that the loss or partial
loss of any one function need not destroy the viability of
future societies.

Such substitute institutions and hypotheses must meet
varying criteria. In general, they must be technically
feasible, politically acceptable, and potentially credible
to the members of the societies that adopt them. Spe-
cifically, they must be characterized as follows:

1. *Economic.*   An acceptable economic surrogate for

the war system will require the expenditure of resources for completely nonproductive purposes at a level comparable to that of the military expenditures otherwise demanded by the size and complexity of each society. Such a substitute system of apparent "waste" must be of a nature that will permit it to remain independent of the normal supply-demand economy; it must be subject to arbitrary political control.

2. *Political.* A viable political substitute for war must posit a generalized external menace to each society of a nature and degree sufficient to require the organization and acceptance of political authority.

3. *Sociological.* First, in the permanent absence of war, new institutions must be developed that will effectively control the socially destructive segments of societies. Second, for purposes of adapting the physical and psychological dynamics of human behavior to the needs of social organization, a credible substitute for war must generate an omnipresent and readily understood fear of personal destruction. This fear must be of a nature and degree sufficient to ensure adherence to societal values to the full extent that they are acknowledged to transcend the value of individual human life.

4. *Ecological.* A substitute for war in its function as the uniquely human system of population control must ensure the survival, if not necessarily the improvement, of the species, in terms of its relation to environmental supply.

5. *Cultural and Scientific.* A surrogate for the function of war as the determinant of cultural values must

establish a basis of sociomoral conflict of equally compelling force and scope. A substitute motivational basis for the quest for scientific knowledge must be similarly informed by a comparable sense of internal necessity.

Substitutes for the Functions of War: Models

The following substitute institutions, among others, have been proposed for consideration as replacements for the nonmilitary functions of war. That they may not have been originally set forth for that purpose does not preclude or invalidate their possible application here.

1. Economic. a) A comprehensive social-welfare program, directed toward maximum improvement of general conditions of human life. b) A giant open-end space research program, aimed at unreachable targets. c) A permanent, ritualized, ultra-elaborate disarmament inspection system, and variants of such a system.

2. Political. a) An omnipresent, virtually omnipotent international police force. b) An established and recognized extraterrestrial menace. c) Massive global environmental pollution. d) Fictitious alternate enemies.

3. Sociological: Control function. a) Programs generally derived from the Peace Corps model. b) A modern, sophisticated form of slavery. *Motivational function.* a) Intensified environmental pollution. b) New religions or other mythologies. c) Socially oriented blood games. d) Combination forms.

4. Ecological. A comprehensive program of applied eugenics.

5. *Cultural.* No replacement institution offered. *Scientific.* The secondary requirements of the space research, social welfare, and/or eugenics programs.

Substitutes for the Functions of War: Evaluation

The models listed above reflect only the beginning of the quest for substitute institutions for the functions of war, rather than a recapitulation of alternatives. It would be both premature and inappropriate, therefore, to offer final judgments on their applicability to a transition to peace and after. Furthermore, since the necessary but complex project of correlating the compatibility of proposed surrogates for different functions could be treated only in exemplary fashion at this time, we have elected to withhold such hypothetical correlations as were tested as statistically inadequate.[1]

Nevertheless, some tentative and cursory comments on these proposed functional "solutions" will indicate the scope of the difficulties involved in this area of peace planning.

Economic. The social-welfare model cannot be expected to remain outside the normal economy after the conclusion of its predominantly capital-investment phase; its value in this function can therefore be only temporary. The space-research substitute appears to meet both major criteria, and should be examined in greater detail, especially in respect to its probable effects on other war functions. "Elaborate inspection" schemes, although superficially attractive, are inconsistent with the basic premise of transition to peace. The "unarmed forces" variant, logistically similar, is subject to the same functional criticism as the general social-welfare model.

Political. Like the inspection-scheme surrogates, proposals for plenipotentiary international police are inherently incompatible with the ending of the war system. The "unarmed forces" variant, amended to include unlimited powers of economic sanction, might conceivably be expanded to constitute a credible external menace. Development of an acceptable threat from "outer space," presumably in conjunction with a space-research surrogate for economic control, appears unpromising in terms of credibility. The environmental-pollution model does not seem sufficiently responsive to immediate social control, except through arbitrary acceleration of current pollution trends; this in turn raises questions of political acceptability. New, less regressive, approaches to the creation of fictitious global "enemies" invite further investigation.

Sociological: Control function. Although the various substitutes proposed for this function that are modeled roughly on the Peace Corps appear grossly inadequate in potential scope, they should not be ruled out without further study. Slavery, in a technologically modern and conceptually euphemized form, may prove a more efficient and flexible institution in this area. *Motivational function.* Although none of the proposed substitutes for war as the guarantor of social allegiance can be dismissed out of hand, each presents serious and special difficulties. Intensified environmental threats may raise ecological dangers; mythmaking dissociated from war may no longer be politically feasible; purposeful blood games and rituals can far more readily be devised than implemented. An institution combining this function with the preceding one, based on, but not necessarily imitative of, the precedent of organized ethnic repression, warrants careful consideration.

Ecological. The only apparent problem in the application of an adequate eugenic substitute for war is that of timing; it cannot be effectuated until the transition to peace has been completed, which involves a serious temporary risk of ecological failure.

Cultural. No plausible substitute for this function of war has yet been proposed. It may be, however, that a basic cultural value-determinant is not necessary to the survival of a stable society. *Scientific.* The same might be said for the function of war as the prime mover of the search for knowledge. However, adoption of either a giant space-research program, a comprehensive social-welfare program, or a master program of eugenic control would provide motivation for limited technologies.

General Conclusions

It is apparent, from the foregoing, that no program or combination of programs yet proposed for a transition to peace has remotely approached meeting the comprehensive functional requirements of a world without war. Although one projected system for filling the economic function of war seems promising, similar optimism cannot be expressed in the equally essential political and sociological areas. The other major nonmilitary functions of war—ecological, cultural, scientific—raise very different problems, but it is at least possible that detailed programming of substitutes in these areas is not prerequisite to transition. More important, it is not enough to develop adequate but separate surrogates for the major war functions; they must be fully compatible and in no degree self-canceling.

Until such a unified program is developed, at least hypothetically, it is impossible for this or any other group to furnish meaningful answers to the questions originally presented to us. When asked how best to prepare for the advent of peace, we must first reply, as strongly as we can, that the war system cannot responsibly be allowed to disappear until 1) we know exactly what it is we plan to put in its place, and 2) we are certain, beyond reasonable doubt, that these substitute institutions will serve their purposes in terms of the survival and stability of society. It will then be time enough to develop methods for effectuating the transition; procedural programming must follow, not precede, substantive solutions.

Such solutions, if indeed they exist, will not be arrived at without a revolutionary revision of the modes of thought heretofore considered appropriate to peace research. That we have examined the fundamental questions involved from a dispassionate, value-free point of view should not imply that we do not appreciate the intellectual and emotional difficulties that must be overcome on all decision-making levels before these questions are generally acknowledged by others for what they are.

They reflect, on an intellectual level, traditional emotional resistance to new (more lethal and thus more "shocking") forms of weaponry. The understated comment of then-Senator Hubert Humphrey on the publication of *On Thermonuclear War* is still very much to the point: "New thoughts, particularly those which appear to contradict current assumptions, are always painful for the mind to contemplate."

Nor, simply because we have not discussed them, do we minimize the massive reconciliation of conflicting interests which domestic as well as international agreement on proceeding toward genuine peace presupposes. This factor was excluded from the purview of our assignment, but we would be remiss if we failed to take it into account. Although no insuperable obstacle lies in the path of reaching such general agreements, formidable short-term private-group and general-class interest in maintaining the war system is well established and widely recognized. The resistance to peace stemming from such interest is only tangential, in the long run, to the basic functions of war, but it will not be easily overcome, in this country or elsewhere. Some observers, in fact, believe that it cannot be overcome at all in our time, that the price of peace is, simply, too high. This bears on our overall conclusions to the extent that timing in the transference to substitute institutions may often be the critical factor in their political feasibility.

It is uncertain, at this time, whether peace will ever be possible. It is far more questionable, by the objective standard of continued social survival rather than that of emotional pacifism, that it would be desirable even if it were demonstrably attainable. The war system, for all its subjective repugnance to important sections of "public opinion," has demonstrated its effectiveness since the beginning of recorded history; it has provided the basis for the development of many impressively durable civilizations, including that which is dominant today. It has consistently provided unambiguous social priorities. It is, on the whole, a known quantity. A viable system of peace, assuming that the great and complex questions of substitute institutions raised in this Report are both soluble and solved, would still constitute a venture into the unknown, with the inevitable risks attendant on the unforeseen, however small and however well hedged.

Government decision-makers tend to choose peace over war whenever a real option exists, because it usually appears to be the "safer" choice. Under most immediate circumstances they are likely to be right. But in terms of long-range social stability, the opposite is true. At our present state of knowledge and reasonable inference, it is the war system that must be identified with stability, the peace system with social speculation, however justifiable the speculation may appear, in terms of subjective moral or emotional values. A nuclear physicist once remarked, in respect to a possible disarmament agreement: "If we could change the world into a world in which no weapons could be made, that would be stabilizing. But agreements we can expect with the Soviets would be destabilizing."[2] The qualification and the bias are equally irrelevant; *any* condition of genuine total peace, however achieved, would be destabilizing until proved otherwise.

If it were necessary at this moment to opt irrevocably for the retention or for the dissolution of the war system, common prudence would dictate the former course. But it is not yet necessary, late as the hour appears. And more factors must eventually enter the war-peace equation than even the most determined search for alternative institutions for the functions of war can be expected to reveal. One group of such factors has been given only passing mention in this Report; it centers around the possible obsolescence of the war system itself. We have noted, for instance, the limitations of the war system in filling its ecological function and the declining importance of this aspect of war. It by no means stretches the imagination to visualize comparable developments which may compromise the efficacy of war as, for example, an economic controller or as an organizer of social allegiance. This kind of possibility, however remote, serves as a reminder that all calculations of contingency not only involve the weighing of one group of risks against another, but require a respectful allowance for error on both sides of the scale.

A more expedient reason for pursuing the investigation of alternate ways and means to serve the current functions of war is narrowly political. It is possible that one or more major sovereign nations may arrive, through ambiguous leadership, at a position in which a ruling administrative class may lose control of basic public opinion or of its ability to rationalize a desired war. It is not hard to imagine, in such circumstance, a situation in which such governments may feel forced to initiate serious full-scale disarmament proceedings (perhaps provoked by "accidental" nuclear explosions), and that such negotiations may lead to the actual disestablishment of military institutions. As our Report has made clear, this could be catastrophic. It seems evident that, in the event an important part of the world is suddenly plunged without sufficient warning into an inadvertent peace, even partial and inadequate preparation for the possibility may be better than none. The difference could even be critical. The models considered in the preceding chapter, both those that seem promising and those that do not, have one positive feature in common—an inherent flexibility of phasing. And despite our strictures against knowingly proceeding into peace-transition procedures without thorough substantive preparation, our government must nevertheless be ready to move in this direction with whatever limited resources of planning are on hand at the time—if circumstances so require. An arbitrary all-or-nothing approach is no more realistic in the development of contingency peace programming than it is anywhere else.

But the principal cause for concern over the continuing effectiveness of the war system, and the more important reason for hedging with peace planning, lies in the backwardness of current war-system programming. Its controls have not kept pace with the technological advances it has made possible. Despite its unarguable success to date, even in this era of unprecedented potential in mass destruction, it continues to operate largely on a laissez-faire basis. To the best of our knowledge, no serious quantified studies have ever been conducted to determine, for example:

—optimum levels of armament production, for purposes of economic control, at any given series of chronological points and under any given relationship between civilian production and consumption patterns;

—correlation factors between draft recruitment policies and mensurable social dissidence;

—minimum levels of population destruction necessary to maintain war-threat credibility under varying political conditions;

—optimum cyclical frequency of "shooting" wars under varying circumstances of historical relationship.

These and other war-function factors are fully susceptible to analysis by today's computer-based systems,[3] but they have not been so treated; modern analytical techniques have up to now been relegated to such aspects of the ostensible functions of war as procurement, personnel deployment, weapons analysis, and the like. We do not disparage these types of application, but only deplore their lack of utilization to greater capacity in attacking problems of broader scope. Our concern for efficiency in this context is not aesthetic, economic, or humanistic. It stems from the axiom that no system can long survive at either input or output levels that consistently or substantially deviate from an optimum range. As their data grow increasingly sophisticated, the war sys-

tem and its functions are increasingly endangered by
such deviations.

Our final conclusion, therefore, is that it will be necessary for our government to plan in depth for two general
contingencies. The first, and lesser, is the possibility of a
viable general peace; the second is the successful con-
tinuation of the war system. In our view, careful preparation for the possibility of peace should be extended, not
because we take the position that the end of war would
necessarily be desirable, if it is in fact possible, but because it may be thrust upon us in some form whether we
are ready for it or not. Planning for rationalizing and
quantifying the war system, on the other hand, to ensure
the effectiveness of its major stabilizing functions, is not
only more promising in respect to anticipated results, but
is essential; we can no longer take for granted that it will
continue to serve our purposes well merely because it
always has. The objective of government policy in regard
to war and peace, in this period of uncertainty, must be
to preserve maximum options. The recommendations
which follow are directed to this end.

SECTION 8

RECOMMENDATIONS

(1) We propose the establishment, under executive order of the President, of a permanent War/Peace Research Agency, empowered and mandated to execute the programs described in (2) and (3) below. This agency (a) will be provided with nonaccountable funds sufficient to implement its responsibilities and decisions at its own discretion, and (b) will have authority to preempt and utilize, without restriction, any and all facilities of the executive branch of the government in pursuit of its objectives. It will be organized along the lines of the National Security Council, except that none of its governing, executive, or operating personnel will hold other public office or governmental responsibility. Its directorate will be drawn from the broadest practicable

spectrum of scientific disciplines, humanistic studies, applied creative arts, operating technologies, and otherwise unclassified professional occupations. It will be responsible solely to the President, or to other officers of government temporarily deputized by him. Its operations will be governed entirely by its own rules of procedure. Its authority will expressly include the unlimited right to withhold information on its activities and its decisions, from anyone except the President, whenever it deems such secrecy to be in the public interest.

(2) THE FIRST OF THE WAR/PEACE RESEARCH AGENCY'S two principal responsibilities will be to determine all that can be known, including what can reasonably be inferred in terms of relevant statistical probabilities, that may bear on an eventual transition to a general condition of peace. The findings in this Report may be considered to constitute the beginning of this study and to indicate its orientation; detailed records of the investigations and findings of the Special Study Group on which this Report is based, will be furnished the agency, along with whatever clarifying data the agency deems necessary. This aspect of the agency's work will hereinafter be referred to as "Peace Research."

The Agency's Peace Research activities will necessarily include, but not be limited to, the following:

(a) The creative development of possible substitute institutions for the principal nonmilitary functions of war.

(b) The careful matching of such institutions against

the criteria summarized in this Report, as refined, revised, and extended by the agency.

(c) The testing and evaluation of substitute institutions, for acceptability, feasibility, and credibility, against hypothecated transitional and postwar conditions; the testing and evaluation of the effects of the anticipated atrophy of certain unsubstituted functions.

(d) The development and testing of the correlativity of multiple substitute institutions, with the eventual objective of establishing a comprehensive program of compatible war substitutes suitable for a planned transition to peace, if and when this is found to be possible and subsequently judged desirable by appropriate political authorities.

(e) The preparation of a wide-ranging schedule of partial, uncorrelated, crash programs of adjustment suitable for reducing the dangers of an unplanned transition to peace effected by *force majeure*.

Peace Research methods will include but not be limited to, the following:

(a) The comprehensive interdisciplinary application of historical, scientific, technological, and cultural data.

(b) The full utilization of modern methods of mathematical modeling, analogical analysis, and other, more sophisticated, quantitative techniques in process of development that are compatible with computer programming.

(c) The heuristic "peace games" procedures developed during the course of its assignment by the Special

Study Group, and further extensions of this basic approach to the testing of institutional functions.

(3) THE WAR/PEACE RESEARCH AGENCY's other principal responsibility will be "War Research." Its fundamental objective will be to ensure the continuing viability of the war system to fulfill its essential nonmilitary functions for as long as the war system is judged necessary to or desirable for the survival of society. To achieve this end, the War Research groups within the agency will engage in the following activities:

(a) *Quantification of existing application of the nonmilitary functions of war.* Specific determinations will include, but not be limited to: 1) the gross amount and the net proportion of nonproductive military expenditures since World War II assignable to the need for war as an economic stabilizer; 2) the amount and proportion of military expenditures and destruction of life, property, and natural resources during this period assignable to the need for war as an instrument for political control; 3) similar figures, to the extent that they can be separately arrived at, assignable to the need for war to maintain social cohesiveness; 4) levels of recruitment and expenditures on the draft and other forms of personnel deployment attributable to the need for military institutions to control social disaffection; 5) the statistical relationship of war casualties to world food supplies; 6) the correlation of military actions and expenditures with cultural activities and scientific advances (including necessarily, the development of mensurable standards in these areas).

(b) *Establishment of a priori modern criteria for the execution of the nonmilitary functions of war.* These will include, but not be limited to: 1) calculation of minimum and optimum ranges of military expenditure required, under varying hypothetical conditions, to fulfill these several functions, separately and collectively; 2) determination of minimum and optimum levels of destruction of life, property, and natural resources prerequisite to the credibility of external threat essential to the political and motivational functions; 3) development of a negotiable formula governing the relationship between military recruitment and training policies and the exigencies of social control.

(c) *Reconciliation of these criteria with prevailing economic, political, sociological, and ecological limitations.* The ultimate object of this phase of War Research is to rationalize the heretofore informal operations of the war system. It should provide practical working procedures through which responsible governmental authority may resolve the following war-function problems, among others, under any given circumstances: 1) how to determine the optimum quantity, nature, and timing of military expenditures to ensure a desired degree of economic control; 2) how to organize the recruitment, deployment, and ostensible use of military personnel to ensure a desired degree of acceptance of authorized social values; 3) how to compute on a short-term basis, the nature and extent of the loss of life and other resources which should be suffered and/or inflicted during any single outbreak of hostilities to achieve a desired degree of internal political authority and social allegiance; 4) how to project, over extended periods, the nature and quality of overt warfare which must be planned and budgeted to achieve a desired degree of contextual stability for the same purpose; factors to be determined must include frequency of occurrence, length of phase, intensity of physical destruction, extensiveness of geographical involvement, and optimum mean loss of life; 5) how to extrapolate accurately from the foregoing, for ecological purposes, the continuing effect of the war system, over such extended cycles, on population pressures, and to adjust the planning of casualty rates accordingly.

War Research procedures will necessarily include, but not be limited to, the following:

(a) The collation of economic, military, and other relevant data into uniform terms, permitting the reversible translation of heretofore discrete categories of information.[1]

(b) The development and application of appropriate forms of cost-effectiveness analysis suitable for adapting such new constructs to computer terminology, programming, and projection.[2]

(c) Extension of the "war games" methods of systems testing to apply, as a quasi-adversary proceeding, to the nonmilitary functions of war.[3]

(4) SINCE BOTH PROGRAMS of the War/Peace Research Agency will share the same purpose—to maintain governmental freedom of choice in respect to war and peace

until the direction of social survival is no longer in doubt —it is of the essence of this proposal that the agency be constituted without limitation of time. Its examination of existing and proposed institutions will be self-liquidating when its own function shall have been superseded by the historical developments it will have, at least in part, initiated.

NOTES

SECTION 1

1. *The Economic and Social Consequences of Disarmament: U.S. Reply to the Inquiry of the Secretary-General of the United Nations* (Washington, D.C.: USGPO, June 1964), pp. 8–9.

2. Herman Kahn, *Thinking About the Unthinkable* (New York: Horizon, 1962), p. 35.

3. Robert S. McNamara, in an address before the American Society of Newspaper Editors, in Montreal, P.Q., Canada, 18 May 1966.

4. Alfred North Whitehead, in "The Anatomy of Some Scientific Ideas," included in *The Aims of Education* (New York: Macmillan, 1929).

5. At Ann Arbor, Michigan, 16 June 1962.

6. Louis J. Halle, "Peace in Our Time? Nuclear Weapons as a Stabilizer," *The New Republic* (28 December 1963).

SECTION 2

1. Kenneth E. Boulding, "The World War Industry as an Economic Problem," in Emile Benoit and Kenneth E. Boulding (eds.), *Disarmament and the Economy* (New York: Harper & Row, 1963).

2. McNamara, in ASNE Montreal address cited.

3. *Report of the Committee on the Economic Impact of Defense and Disarmament* (Washington: USGPO, July 1965).

4. Sumner M. Rosen, "Disarmament and the Economy," *War/Peace Report* (March 1966).

SECTION 3

1. *Vide* William D. Grampp, "False Fears of Disarmament," *Harvard Business Review* (Jan.-Feb. 1964) for a concise example of this reasoning.

2. Seymour Melman, "The Cost of Inspection for Disarmament," in Benoit and Boulding, *op. cit.*

SECTION 5

1. Arthur I. Waskow, *Toward the Unarmed Forces of the United States* (Washington: Institute for Policy Studies, 1966), p. 9. (This is the unabridged edition of the text of a report and proposal prepared for a seminar of strategists and Congressmen in 1965; it was later given limited distribution among other persons engaged in related projects.)

2. David T. Bazelon, "The Politics of the Paper Economy," *Commentary* (November 1962), p. 409.

3. *The Economic Impact of Disarmament* (Washington: USGPO, January 1962).

4. David T. Bazelon, "The Scarcity Makers," *Commentary* (October 1962), p. 298.

5. Frank Pace, Jr., in an address before the American Bankers' Association, September 1957.

6. A random example, taken in this case from a story by David Deitch in the New York *Herald Tribune* (9 February 1966).

7. *Vide* L. Gumplowicz, in *Geschichte der Staatstheorien* (Innsbruck: Wagner, 1905) and earlier writings.

8. K. Fischer, *Das Militär* (Zurich: Steinmetz Verlag, 1932), pp. 42–43.

9. The obverse of this phenomenon is responsible for the principal combat problem of present-day infantry offi-

cers: the unwillingness of otherwise "trained" troops to fire at an enemy close enough to be recognizable as an individual rather than simply as a target.

10. Herman Kahn, *On Thermonuclear War* (Princeton, N.J.: Princeton University Press, 1960), p. 42.

11. John D. Williams, "The Nonsense about Safe Driving," *Fortune* (September 1958).

12. *Vide* most recently K. Lorenz, in *Das Sogenannte Böse: zur Naturgeschichte der Aggression* (Vienna: G. Borotha-Schoeler Verlag, 1964).

13. Beginning with Herbert Spencer and his contemporaries, but largely ignored for nearly a century.

14. As in recent draft-law controversy, in which the issue of selective deferment of the culturally privileged is often carelessly equated with the preservation of the biologically "fittest."

15. G. Bouthoul, in *La Guerre* (Paris: Presses universitaires de France, 1953) and many other more detailed studies. The useful concept of "polemology," for the study of war as an independent discipline, is his, as is the notion of "demographic relaxation," the sudden temporary decline in the rate of population increase after major wars.

16. This seemingly premature statement is supported by one of our own test studies. But it hypothecates both the stabilizing of world population growth and the institution of fully adequate environmental controls. Under these two conditions, the probability of the permanent elimination of involuntary global famine is 68 percent by 1976 and 95 percent by 1981.

SECTION 6

1. This round figure is the median taken from our compu-

tations, which cover varying contingencies, but it is sufficient for the purpose of general discussion.

2. But less misleading than the more elegant traditional metaphor, in which war expenditures are referred to as the "ballast" of the economy but which suggests incorrect quantitative relationships.

3. Typical in generality, scope, and rhetoric. We have not used any published program as a model; similarities are unavoidably coincidental rather than tendentious.

4. *Vide* the reception of a "Freedom Budget for all Americans," proposed by A. Philip Randolph *et al;* it is a ten-year plan, estimated by its sponsors to cost $185 billion.

5. Waskow, *op. cit.*

6. By several current theorists, most extensively and effectively by Robert R. Harris in *The Real Enemy,* an unpublished doctoral dissertation made available to this study.

7. In ASNE Montreal address cited.

8. *The Tenth Victim.*

9. For an examination of some of its social implications, see Seymour Rubenfeld, *Family of Outcasts: A New Theory of Delinquency* (New York: Free Press, 1965).

10. As in Nazi Germany; this type of "ideological" ethnic repression, directed to specific sociological ends, should not be confused with traditional economic exploitation, as of Negroes in the U.S., South Africa, etc.

11. By teams of experimental biologists in Massachusetts, Michigan, and California, as well as in Mexico and the U.S.S.R. Preliminary test applications are scheduled in Southeast Asia, in countries not yet announced.

12. Expressed in the writings of H. Marshall McLuhan, in

Understanding Media: The Extensions of Man (New York: McGraw-Hill, 1964) and elsewhere.

13. This rather optimistic estimate was derived by plotting a three-dimensional distribution of three arbitrarily defined variables; the macro-structural, relating to the extension of knowledge beyond the capacity of conscious experience; the organic, dealing with the manifestations of terrestrial life as inherently comprehensible; and the infra-particular, covering the subconceptual requirements of natural phenomena. Values were assigned to the known and unknown in each parameter, tested against data from earlier chronologies, and modified heuristically until predictable correlations reached a useful level of accuracy. "Two decades" means, in this case, 20.6 years, with a standard deviation of only 1.8 years. (An incidental finding, not pursued to the same degree of accuracy, suggests a greatly accelerated resolution of issues in the biological sciences after 1972.)

SECTION 7

1. Since they represent an examination of too small a percentage of the eventual options, in terms of "multiple mating," the subsystem we developed for this application. But an example will indicate how one of the most frequently recurring correlation problems—chronological phasing—was brought to light in this way. One of the first combinations tested showed remarkably high coefficients of compatibility, on a *post hoc* static basis, but no variations of timing, using a thirty-year transition module, permitted even marginal synchronization. The combination was thus disqualified. This would not rule out the possible adequacy of combinations using modifications of the same factors, however, since minor variations in a proposed final condition may have disproportionate effects on phasing.

108   THE REPORT

2. Edward Teller, quoted in *War/Peace Report* (December 1964).

3. E.g., the highly publicized "Delphi technique" and other, more sophisticated procedures. A new system, especially suitable for institutional analysis, was developed during the course of this study in order to hypothecate mensurable "peace games"; a manual of this system is being prepared and will be submitted for general distribution among appropriate agencies. For older, but still useful, techniques, see Norman C. Dalkey's *Games and Simulations* (Santa Monica, Calif.: Rand, 1964).

SECTION 8

1. A primer-level example of the obvious and long overdue need for such translation is furnished by Kahn (in *Thinking About the Unthinkable*, p. 102). Under the heading "Some Awkward Choices" he compares four hypothetical policies: a certain loss of $3,000; a .1 chance of loss of $300,000; a .01 chance of loss of $30,000,000; and a .001 chance of loss of $3,000,000,000. A government decision-maker would "very likely" choose in that order. But what if "lives are at stake rather than dollars"? Kahn suggests that the order of choice would be reversed, although current experience does not support this opinion. Rational war research can and must make it possible to express, without ambiguity, lives in terms of dollars and vice versa; the choices need not be, and cannot be, "awkward."

2. Again, an overdue extension of an obvious application of techniques up to now limited to such circumscribed purposes as improving kill-ammunition ratios determining local choice between precision and saturation bombing, and other minor tactical, and occasionally strategic, ends. The slowness of Rand, I.D.A., and other responsible analytic organizations to extend cost-effectiveness

and related concepts beyond early-phase applications has already been widely remarked on and critized elsewhere.

3. The inclusion of institutional factors in war-game techniques has been given some rudimentary consideration in the Hudson Institute's *Study for Hypothetical Narratives for Use in Command and Control Systems Planning* (by William Pfaff and Edmund Stillman; Final report published 1963). But here, as with other war and peace studies to date, what has blocked the logical extension of new analytic techniques has been a general failure to understand and properly evaluate the non-military functions of war.